OTHER BOOKS BY ALEXANDER KING

Mine Enemy Grows Older

May This House Be Safe from Tigers

Peter Altenberg's Evocations of Love

I Should Have Kissed Her More

The Great Ker-Plunk

IS THERE
A LIFE
AFTER
BIRTH?

---

by Alexander King

1963

SIMON AND SCHUSTER
NEW YORK

LIBRARY OF CONGRESS CATALOG CARD NUMBER: 63-9278

MANUFACTURED IN THE UNITED STATES OF AMERICA

PRINTED BY THE MURRAY PRINTING COMPANY

BOUND BY H. WOLFF

To Margie, who stood by patiently and lovingly, without ever trying to make helpful suggestions.

Love work, hate tyranny, live right-
eously, and don't let your name become
too well known to the authorities!

—RABBI SHEMAIAH

50 B.C.

CHAPTER ONE

W<small>HEN</small> <small>I</small> <small>WAS</small> seven years old I was expelled from my first Viennese grammar school. The official charge was "Unaccountable Conduct."

In later life I drew some comfort out of the knowledge that in the thirteenth century the great Roger Bacon had been sentenced to fifteen years in prison and the charge which had landed him there was "Entertaining Heretical Frivolities."

Bacon actually got a lot of people set against him when he outlined certain seemingly logical measures to produce mechanically propelled boats; he also experimented rather recklessly with the explosive possibilities of gunpowder, and he finally managed to lose everybody's confidence in the soundness of his mind by seriously setting about to construct some rudimentary flying machines.

I will not pretend that my own trespasses against the public goodwill were of an equally revolutionary nature, but I do maintain that I, too, very dramatically demonstrated, quite early in life, that the easiest thing in the world to achieve is the effective disapproval of any sort of uncritically vested authority. Roger Bacon had outraged the patience of an all-powerful church. I, on the other hand, had brought a condition of absolutely vitriolic rancor into the turgid mind of a middle-aged Austrian school supervisor.

I was being ejected out of this truly sinister emporium by Doktor Gerhardt Hanslicht, the dean of a pedagogical chicken coop which housed about a hundred and fifty frightened children, half a dozen or so unwashed, hypocritical and miserably underpaid teachers and their three and a half totally stupefied assistants. (That half of an assistant had lost one leg, one arm and a large part of his skull when a demented army veteran had brought along some real bullets to a public shooting gallery.)

I remember the Herr Doktor as clearly as if it had all just happened last week. I even recall with uncommon precision his grimy private office, with its overpowering smell of mildewed linoleum, in which our final interview took place. I must confess that I had always hated this odious creature with all the passionate concentration of my childish heart, and, like all the rest of my fellow students, I was firmly convinced that he went to bed every night with all of his clothes on—frock coat, striped trousers, congress gaiters and all the rest of it. We simply couldn't imagine Hanslicht naked. Even our feverishly overactive imaginations were fragmented into chaos when we tried to conceive of him undressed.

So there we stood in that ghastly, oak-paneled mausoleum of his—my tear-stained mother, my serious-looking, puzzled father and I, with my eyeballs rolled appealingly upward (an effect I had originally observed and copied from an angel out of a bas-relief by Luca della Robbia).

Of course I was fully aware that it was already much too late to expect favorable results from anything I might possibly do to ingratiate myself with the monster; nevertheless, I assumed a carefully calculated infantile posture of pigeon-toed helplessness and, what's more, distinctly recall that although I realized that no one was paying the slightest attention to me I was determined to carry through the role of *Injured Innocence* even if just for my own amusement alone. It was a true case of art for art's sake, and I had an absolute ball with it.

The Herr Doktor, who looked at the world through pince-nez glasses, had his skimpy hair standing wildly on end, and I realized again for perhaps the hundredth time how much that mop of reddish-gray fuzz on top of his head resembled the raveled coxcomb of an impotent rooster. However, this was the first time I had ever seen him in complete profile, and I noticed with a shock that his eyes hung so far out of their sockets that they actually looked like a wilting pair of pulpy binoculars.

For quite a long while there was total silence in that depressing room, and although, as I've already told you, nobody gave me the slightest tumble I went right on with my cherubic eye-rolling —until Doktor Hanslicht suddenly gave an enormous cough, eructed a great wad of phlegm out of his gravel pit and, finally, after having disposed of the result in a piece of crumpled writing paper, turned his glowering orbs fully toward my father and said, "I believe that this fellow"—pointing, but not looking, at me— "this fellow belongs, or ought to be placed, in a very strict corrective institution. I think he ought not to be permitted to run loose with other normal children at all."

Later on, I learned *where* and *how* the Herr Doktor had acquired the peculiar voice and special style of diction which he brought into play whenever he happened to lose his temper. He had learned it all from a particularly brutal drill sergeant who had tyrannized mercilessly over the Herr Doktor while he had been undergoing his compulsory military training some thirty-five years before, somewhere on the outer borders of Transylvania. Well, now he let me, and my poor parents, have it with the compound interest of the pent-up rage and frustration which were the chronic concomitants of his whole ghastly existence. Abjectly servile and blindly domineering by turns, he was the victim of a truly heraldic bureaucracy whose duplicates, even in those dark days of scholastic enslavement, flourished only in Greater Germany and within the knout-oriented confines of Czarist Russia.

This creature's total humanity had finally shrunk down to a mere blind affection for a permanently molting, female canary. He did raise his myopic sights *just once* and make a wild stab at enlarging his emotional investments to plutocratic dimensions— but I'll tell you more about that in just a moment.

Meanwhile, we're still standing in the dim light of the frigid execution chamber, and Doktor Hanslicht proceeds as follows: "I must tell you, with all the authority which I derive from my long years in the teaching profession in the kingdom of Austria and my experience in the armed forces of our exalted Emperor, Francis Joseph the Second, that this *fellow*"—another wave of his arm in my direction—"this *fellow* is most certainly headed for a very, very dark future. It is no pleasure for me to make such an ominous prognostication to any parent, but I think you can clearly see that the facts speak for themselves!"

If the facts actually spoke for themselves, they certainly never made themselves coherently audible to my poor parents, because, when I asked them after a while what "Unaccountable Conduct" signified, I found that my shattered elders had not been able to penetrate to the meaning behind this cryptic charge either.

At any rate, Doktor Gerhardt Hanslicht died of an occlusion of the brain about a year later, and I'm afraid that some of our relatives and friends were firmly convinced that my short apprenticeship at his dismal barracks had been a large contributing factor to his demise.

I'm certainly sorry he died so soon. I would have liked to send him a few of my current press clippings, which, in some instances, seem to verify his most depressing predictions about my future.

As a matter of fact, I knew perfectly well at the time what particular actions on my part had so totally dismantled Doktor Hanslicht's precarious academic poise.

You see, I had an art teacher, a Miss Lenwald—whose first name was Helen—who had deep, velvet-brown eyes and long, ash-blond hair. I never doubted that Leda was her mother and that Zeus, in the guise of an enamored swan, had been her sire. At the age of seven I had already long forsaken the hortatory tales of the Old Testament for the more entertaining and frivolous activities of the Olympian Areopagus, and Helen Lenwald seemed to me a living personification to justify the ancient gods for their frequent extracurricular involvements with a number of particularly seductive earthly women.

I absolutely adored her.

She wore the heavy strands of her tightly plaited hair like two stylized halos around her exquisitely modeled head, and it was her dear conceit to hold these braids securely in place by means of eight beautifully veined tortoiseshell hairpins. I had counted these fortunate contrivances many, many times, and on one heart-thumping occasion, while she was correcting one of my drawings, I had even successfully managed to abduct one of these special treasures. This priceless artifact became the cornerstone of a small museum of seemingly trivial memorabilia whose dominating interest, for me, lay in the fact that they bore some—no matter how collaterally relative—connection to my goddess.

And then, one afternoon, during our final period in school, I had managed, by some pretext or another, to remain longer in Miss Lenwald's classroom than the rest of her students. At last she said to me: "Don't you think you'd better run along now, before your mother gets worried?"

"Oh, she doesn't worry about me," I said. "She knows that I like to help you with the sorting of the drawing materials."

"Nevertheless," she said, "it is half-past four and I think you had better go home now."

So I went up to the desk and handed her some art materials I had been labeling and cataloguing for her, and for one long, blissful moment I stood close beside her and inhaled the magical fragrance of her intoxicating presence. Only seven tortoiseshell pins shimmered darkly in her pale, honey-colored tresses, and, as usual, she also wore a tiny brooch in the shape of a butterfly just a little above her heart. It was pinned onto her high-necked, lace-trimmed blouse, and never before had I been able to observe

13

it so closely. I watched, almost hypnotically, as this minute, jeweled insect undulated ever so gently with the ebb and tide of her breathing, and it may well have been some extrasensory element in the feverish concentration of my not altogether childish stare which caused her suddenly to rise, turn around to me and take my hand.

"Tell me, Alexander," she said, "what would you really like to be, if you had your choice?"

Without hesitating for a moment, I said, "Miss Lenwald, I would like to be *that butterfly.*"

She blushed as nobody nowadays blushes any longer, gave an embarrassed laugh and pressed my burning face, for a brief eternity, up against the yielding texture of her womanly softness.

And that was all.

Excepting only that at that very moment both of us became aware that Doktor Hanslicht had been quietly watching us from the doorway. As I looked at him I realized with sickening certainty that my days in the shadow of my beloved could indeed be counted among the digits of a single hand.

You see, even the biggest numskulls among my fellow students were well aware that our popeyed superintendent had a howling crush on our lovely art teacher. I daresay even his poor, bare-assed canary had gotten wise to it by then. Yes, Hanslicht, the incorruptible ramrod, was head over heels in love with the only live human being who taught in that moldy school of his. His unconcealable embarrassment whenever he came into her presence provided the very few grotesquely cheerful moments among our scholastic ordeals. It was equally clear to all of us that Miss Lenwald simply couldn't abide the sight of him.

And that, as I have told it here, was the true state of affairs which brought about my expulsion from that ugly, mottled-gray building in the Disterweggasse, in Vienna, in the year of our Lord 1907.

Later, after I had left the school and was attending the Jesuit institution where some of the happiest and most rewarding years of my life were to be spent, I accidentally happened to encounter Miss Lenwald in a pastry shop right near my home.

She was charming, of course, and since I luckily had quite a bit of change in my pocket she even grudgingly allowed me to buy her two of my favorite confections.

"I miss you greatly," she said. "You were my most talented student; and I know that you really love art."

"Thank you," I said, "and how is Doktor Hanslicht these days?"

"He hasn't been too well lately," she said. "You know, his canary died this spring, and Doktor Ehrenreich has been taking Doktor Hanslicht's place during the past two months."

She was wearing a coarsely woven, pale-blue straw hat from which a thin gray veil made a halfhearted attempt to conceal her features; and it was through this veil that I could see the blood rising to her sweet face as she impulsively put her hand on my shoulder. "Tell me," she said, "you don't happen to have a tortoiseshell hairpin that might match the ones I always use? You see, my mother gave them to me when I graduated from high school. She bought them once, long ago, during a vacation in Karlsbad, and they really mean a great deal to me."

I stared at her, flame-faced on my own account, but she went right on talking. "I tell you what," she said. "Remember the little butterfly you seemed to fancy so much? Would you like to have that? I'll be glad to send it to you."

"Oh, really, Miss Lenwald," I said. "I'm terribly ashamed. I should have returned your property a long time ago but . . ."

"Don't even think of it," she said. "That little butterfly brooch has no special significance at all, and I'll be very glad to let you have it. I hardly ever wear it nowadays. Please?!"

"I will mail you the hairpin tomorrow, without fail," I said. Then I kissed her gloved hand, and as I bent over to do so I realized in helpless rage that my eyes were brimming over with childish tears.

CHAPTER TWO

I N THE ENSUING pages my personal experiment in autobiography comes to an end. This happens despite the fact that
I still have notes, diaries, and letters available which would make
it possible for me to fill at least another four good-sized volumes
with material both relevant and interesting on the subject of my
career as an artist and writer during more than half a century.
The reason I have decided to call a halt is simply because I feel
that I shall perhaps never again be so exuberantly in control of
the factual and emotional context of my past as I am at this particular point of time, and also, because I have finally become
most impatient to give some sort of intellectual and even philosophical summation of my dominating feelings and attitudes toward varied aspects of our contemporary world.

I have often, in my other writings, deliberately suppressed a
good many urgently felt critical opinions since I was, above all,
most anxious to present some sort of cogent panorama of the

passing scene as it had come to affect me during the six decades of my human awareness.

You see, it occurred to me very early in life that *I* and a *very, very few* other people were *reasonable beings*, in an otherwise totally *unreasonable* scheme of things.

So when I first sat down to perpetrate an autobiography, I proceeded to busy myself in marshaling endless platoons of more or less chronological data which I hoped would demonstrate as effectively as possible the fantastic imbalance between my own hopes and aspirations and the aims of a largely blind, almost totally deaf and altogether frenziedly preoccupied mass of humanity that seethed in endless confusion all about me.

I am well aware that the lines I have just written could very easily have been penned by any number of sensitive adolescents who are condemned to look upon the world in a state of chronic consternation, but what I am saying here is not just meant to be a testimonial to my vivid memory of my own bewildering young manhood, because, as a matter of fact, the confusion between the things which *seem*, and the things that *are*, has continued in all its complexity throughout the dizzily passing decades and, in many instances, I am at this very moment as deeply puzzled by many aspects of human behavior as I was when I had just turned sixteen.

Therefore, it is my intention in the following chapters to examine the reasons for the seemingly relentless bedevilment which falls upon each new generation as it stumbles along, with fatal momentum, toward an almost invariably frustrating maturity.

Of course, I still have a great number of illustrative tales and anecdotes to tell about the many strange people who embittered or enlivened my blundering days and who tormented or consoled the darkness of my nights according to the peculiar tempers of their unpredictable inclinations.

Something else is on my mind: during the past four and a half years some forty thousand people have found themselves impelled to communicate with me through the mails. Well, a good many of these letters which I received were certainly pretty upsetting. Most of the writers were evidently bothered by *something*, and the reason they sent word to *me* was not at all because they believed that I was *able* or *willing* to give them any kind of help at all.

Not a bit of it.

I think they just wanted to unburden their minds to someone who sounded as if he might be sympathetic even toward people who hadn't really *failed* at anything—who had, in fact, made out tolerably well in life, and yet felt that somewhere along the line they had been gypped; somewhere along the rocky road to oblivion they had taken the wrong turn and wound up with a decent enough home, a devoted husband and half a dozen apple-cheeked children.

That's right!

Most of these midnight scriveners were *women*, and this only proves my long-standing contention that the ladies in our midst keep on searching their hearts even while cleaning house, or washing a lot of dirty diapers—and they go on doing this long after the dear men of their choice have carefully tucked their unfulfilled dreams into their pockets and have swapped their castles in Spain for just a couple of nights a week at a neighborhood bowling alley.

You can take my word for it: it isn't easy to give advice to a lot of total strangers who are reasonably solvent and who, above everything else, claim that life has been really very good to them. Actually quite a number of my correspondents wrote rather long letters, and before they finally got around to signing their names most of them had, somehow or other, managed quite sensibly to answer their own questions.

Believe me, they didn't puzzle me in the least. I really know all about them. They know quite a lot about me, too. They wrote because they just hoped I'd be especially qualified to understand their crazy dilemmas since I'd given them so many examples out of my own past when I had been stumped by circumstances which were neither particularly dramatic nor especially unendurable.

They were quite right.

Although I am almost a kind of a leftover from another century, I *am* peculiarly endowed to sympathize with the well-fed, the soundly shod, and the comfortably housed emotional derelicts who flounder all around me in truly alarming profusion.

That's the reason I picked such a title for my book in the first place: because I'm not at all convinced that the men and women I run into every day and every year of my life have actually achieved what *I* would call an altogether worthwhile and completely self-fulfilling tenure of human existence.

Not by a damned sight!

CHAPTER THREE

BUT MY OWN historical self-revelations demand attention at this moment, and so, with only seeming irrelevance, I will take you back again to the very beginning of this century when I was a child in Vienna.

As I have indicated before, my origins were of a rather unusual nature; I was a prematurely born infant, and because my parents were middle-aged at the time of my emergence and I was an only child, they were in many ways not particularly well equipped to exert any consistent sort of authority over me. I think that the absence of such authority was a rather critical hiatus in my upbringing, since it is my belief that the domestic supervision and training of an infant ought not to be determined too largely by the infant itself.

Like most children I was, of course, a naturally gifted psychologist, and I can only tell you that I studied the grownups around me with unbelievable shrewdness. This means that, after a while, a sort of fairly livable working arrangement came to exist between myself and the various admonitors upon whom I depended for my survival, and it was only much later in life that I discovered that my dear, dear mother had at all times been fully aware of even my most cunningly staged machinations. Actually, it just happened to suit her peculiar temperament to let me manage a good part of our family relationships in my own special way, but if I ever transgressed too far against decency or common sense, her disapproval descended on me in such unmistakable terms that, whether I liked it or not, I finally had to concede that my parents did possess absolute authority in certain directions where my own sweet will could not yet successfully prevail.

This did not happen very often, by the way, since, as I've already told you, I had observed the behavior patterns of my elders to such good purpose that I could easily foresee when the limits of their patience were likely to be reached and I knew quite enough to curtail my often splenetic and willful behavior before this breaking point was actually achieved.

All this changed a great deal—that is to say, my entire view of life became altered (and, I believe, humanized)—when I was five years old and my mother began to read to me some stories out of the Old Testament. I must hastily insert here that my conversion was a purely literary and not at all a religious one. Also, a significant correction is in order: You see, at my special behest, my mother always read me *the same story* over and over again, since I simply couldn't bear to be separated from those darling protagonists who had all become so intimately familiar to me.

This story was the wonderful legend of Joseph and His Brethren. I had an unappeasable appetite for that particular tale, and because my mother was a very sentimental woman, she always broke into tears when Joseph (after becoming second only to Pharaoh in the land of Egypt) suddenly disclosed his true identity to his treacherous brothers.

At this dramatic juncture the both of us generally cried so much that we were absolutely unable to go on with the reading. It was not until many years later that I came to the realization that this story had a happy ending, since, by tacit agreement, our literary afternoons had always terminated in a flood of tears.

A short while after these Biblical sessions had begun I started to collect cardboard soldiers, which were printed in colorful sheets and sold in heavenly smelling stationery stores all around our neighborhood. I used to cut them out very meticulously with a pair of my mother's discarded scissors and set them up in national and regimental units along the broad windowsills of my playroom.

I cannot resist telling you something about those stationery stores of my Viennese childhood. Plastics had not yet been invented, so everything in those magical shops was *real*. Wood was *wood*, paper was *paper*, and all the toys were made out of real substances and painted by hand. When I think back on my early visits to these places I often fall into reveries so profound that they practically amount to protracted nostalgic seizures. I remember all the blond, the brunette and the dark pencils, neatly stacked in their boxes, from which emanated the decent, reassuring odors of cedarwood, and I tell you that even the smell of the real organic glue that held all those clean, virginal pads and books so firmly together used to give my young heart such a thrill of expectancy, such a feeling of unutterable joy, that the mere recollection of it all is like a benign immersion in a health-giving stream.

Later on, of course, there came the headier aromas of the bookshops and the art-supply stores, and, whenever I think back on those early days, it all adds up to a symphony of odors whose chief theme was the *immanently miraculous*, which was constantly hovering on the brink of my daily horizon.

But why go on? I'll just make myself miserable over it. I had better continue with my yarn.

At any rate, I had a friend at that time who lived next door to us on the treelined Hietzinger Hauptstrasse, and this little boy's name was Albert Klaar. He was a dark-eyed, fair-skinned, sensitive child, as I remember him, and *he*, also, owned quite a large collection of paper soldiers. It stands to reason that, after a while, we began in various small ways to compete with one another;

that is to say, if one of us happened, by chance, to discover some military nationals which the other one didn't yet possess, it was always something of a triumph and certainly an occasion for a bit of crowing on the part of the fortunate collector who had successfully managed to pull off so sensational a scoop.

Well, one afternoon in late spring my mother and I had gone for a long walk and landed in quite an unfamiliar part of the city. It was a rather run-down neighborhood, but what made it particularly exciting for me was that a great many shops had spilled some of the overflow from their colorful inventories right out on the sidewalks in front of their doors. After we had been browsing among this fascinating mercantile debris for quite a while, I suddenly observed, with a thrill that only a true collector can possibly understand, that in the grimy window of a derelict stationery shop a number of unfamiliar cardboard soldiers had been put on display.

I was absolutely jubilant.

"Mamma, Mamma!" I screamed. "They have Japanese soldiers in that window. Nobody I know has Japanese soldiers! Please, please buy me some!"

After my mother had obtained me my heart's desire, she looked at the little watch which was pinned to the jacket of her tailored suit and said: "We'll have to hurry home now or we'll be late for supper."

I was so completely happy with my sensational find (they were samurai warriors decked out in medieval armor, and I had never seen their like before) that I offered no objections at all when she suggested that we terminate our little excursion. But after we had walked on for a few blocks I suddenly stopped and said: "Mamma, can we please go back again to that stationery store?"

"Go back? What for?" said my mother. "You've got your Japanese soldiers, haven't you? Why do you want to go back?"

"I think, Mamma," I said, "I think I would like to buy a card of Japanese soldiers for Albert, too. I don't think he'll ever have a chance to get around to this neighborhood. Is that all right, Mamma?"

My mother looked at me thoughtfully for a moment; then she took me by the hand and we purposefully retraced our steps.

Many years later, when my mother was ill and I sat at her bedside in New York, we happened to be talking of our old life in Vienna.

"I remember one day," she said, "when you found some Japanese soldiers which no shop in our own neighborhood had for sale and, after I'd bought them for you, you decided we should go back to the store and buy some of them, also, for your little friend Albert Klaar. He was your greatest rival in collecting those cardboard soldiers. Remember?"

"Yes, Mother," I said, "I remember it well."

"I thought of that afternoon often, afterward," she said, "because I'm sure I was much remiss in my duties as a mother. I frequently reproached myself about it, too. But that afternoon when you went back to get those Japanese soldiers for Albert I said to myself, 'Well, today his human soul has finally been born, and perhaps, from now on, everything will be just a little easier.'"

A year later I was up against Doktor Gerhardt Hanslicht.

CHAPTER FOUR

A HELL OF A LOT of water has flowed down the Danube since I was a boy, and I often sit and speculate about what could possibly have happened to all of the people whom I knew during those long lost years in the Vienna of my childhood.

I daresay the sudden transference from that life to the New York of my adolescence was perhaps the most shattering single event of my whole existence. The immigrant's traumas are like the aftereffects of a second birth, only nobody swaddles or feeds you or gives a damn what really happens to you. Believe me, it's quite a bit of something. The wonder of it is that anybody ever manages to survive it with even a small fragment of sanity left at all.

A couple of weeks after I'd landed in the United States I made a friend, a boy who lived on the same block with me and whose name was Walter Portson. His people had come out of Scandinavia somewhere and had brought Walter along when he was just a few months old. He was really a decent kid, and he tried to do his best to help get me over the most awkward stages of my foreignness. I liked him a lot, and we kept track of each other for quite a number of years. In fact, we went on waving to one another in a friendly way even over long distances until suddenly, sometime in 1939, his widow, Mildred, asked me to come to his funeral.

Well, anyway, during those first few weeks of our acquaintance he did his tactful best to wise me up, to lift me out of the darkness of my greenhorn status and to make me as acceptably American as everybody else.

"Let's play ball," he said to me one afternoon. "Let's buy a ball and play catch."

"Fine," I said.

So the both of us went into a most unmemorable stationery and candy store, and for three cents we bought a ball.

Come to think of it, that stationery store wasn't so *un*memorable after all. I can remember that one hot day I walked into its characterless dinginess and said to the old man behind the counter, "Please give me a small chocolate soda."

"What flavor?" he said.

So, you see, he didn't actually live for nothing, since after half a century I can still recall his peculiar condition.

By the way, this ball that we purchased was called "Bully Boy," and its name was stamped right on its unresilient exterior in black ink. I noticed at once that there was an absolutely leaden weightfulness about this ball of ours, and when I tried to bounce it off the sidewalk it just lay there like a bull turd.

Now, let's get this thing clear.

Boys in Europe hardly ever played ball at all. They played soccer of course, avidly and passionately, and once in a while, just to oblige some particularly attractive girl friends, they'd even condescend to toss a few rubber balls around with them, in the park somewhere, but—you may believe me—those balls of theirs didn't even have the vaguest resemblance to anything like "Bully Boy."

26

Those balls in the old country were called *Salon Ballen* and were about the size of a full-grown cantaloupe, and most of them were decoratively pasted together out of red and black strips of latex. They were not too tightly filled with air either, and when they bounced off anything they went "boing," ever so softly, like a dowager's bosom that has accidentally come into momentary collision with a marquetry table.

Well, my friend Walter was standing about thirty feet away from me when this ball game of ours began and, without a word of warning, he suddenly hurled this "Bully Boy" straight at me. Luckily, I was always rather agile in those days, because if I hadn't gotten out of the way of that missile he would probably have nailed me right up against the wall of the house in front of which I had taken my stance.

After a while, he showed me a small leather-covered mattress that fitted awkwardly over your hand and with which you were supposed to catch these deadly projectiles. I can assure you that I realized then and there that my days of Austrian daydreaming were definitely over, once and for all.

A country in which children were encouraged to hurl "Bully Boys" at each other required a posture and an attitude for which, certainly, nothing in my past had properly prepared me. Yes, sir, if a mildly disguised rock was considered an amiable plaything in this new land of mine, I had better readjust my sights and my bearings and learn to get a hell of a lot tougher than I had ever imagined I need be.

But ball playing wasn't the only startling novelty I encountered right off. There were lots of other surprises and astonishing contradictions waiting to be assimilated by me.

For instance, I was enormously puzzled by the kids I came to know later on in school, because a good many of them who were already fifteen and sixteen years old were still so confoundedly ignorant on a subject like sex. If the matter ever came up at all, they just sniggered like a bunch of half-wits, and even the more intelligent ones among them became obviously quite embarrassed.

It didn't take me too long to discover the reason for all this.

I found that although the streets of our neighborhood were full of pregnant women and the cats and dogs of the town were feverishly fornicating all around us, the citizens of this great republic had decided, seemingly by common consent, that sex was, by and large, something secret and sordid or that it was, at best, an extremely recondite ritual only clandestinely indulged in by some especially licensed initiates. Furthermore, it was considered the height of bad taste and, to a certain degree, even dangerously antisocial to discuss any aspects of sex with young people on any levels, excepting from those thunder-and-brimstone platforms where the horrors of syphilis and gonorrhea were delineated with meticulous, clinical detail and properly anathematized before an audience consisting *exclusively of males.*

Women were not supposed to know about such things at all, and the belief was certainly held and widely encouraged that no decent girl would ever show the slightest curiosity about such subjects.

As Jimmy Durante would say, "Those were the conditions that prevailed."

I had had a much better break, of course, simply because European kids from the middle-class category to which I belonged could hardly get into their teens without knowing at least as much as the birds and the bees, even in those benighted times. I was also particularly fortunate, because my sensible and loving parents had given me the chance to find out about these critical facts of life without having to obtain such information in its most degrading aspects from a foulmouthed slum urchin or some slavering, hydrocephalic farm yokel.

I recall that one day when I was still extremely young, I introduced some aspect of sex as a conversational gambit. My mother, showing neither surprise nor indignation, took a pencil out of her sewing basket and, on the back of a laundry pad which happened to be lying on the table, she made me a drawing of an inverted bottle and told me, without the slightest embarrassment to either of us, that this, in a rather simplified form, represented a woman's uterus, in which babies were conceived. Briefly, she also outlined for me the particularly volatile and ambitious nature of the male spermatozoa, and when that short period of elucidation was over I was possessed of a damned sight more wholesome information on the subject of sex than most of the men and women who were graduating from high schools in New York City during some of those good old days.

I suppose these intimately personal questions have to be tackled according to the highly individual concepts of morality that prevail within each family unit. However, there can be no doubt that in all matters pertaining to sex the majority of people are influenced by the general climate of ethical prejudices and predilections which, sometimes quite irrationally, happen to dominate within a specific geographic community.

I witnessed a particularly fascinating example of peculiarly national mores when I was living in France some years ago.

My wife and I were staying in an apartment, and although we had a competent maid and had most of our meals at home, we had fallen into the habit of taking dinner, from time to time, in a pleasant little cookshop in one of the side streets near the Quai Voltaire. Since it was quite close to our home, we used to go there at least once a week and, after a while, we managed to be accepted on really friendly terms by the owners of this establishment, and even the poisonously parochial clientele showed a certain tolerant acquiescence toward our presence in their midst. We had reached a point where nobody gave any outward signs of astonishment when we appeared and we were treated with the quiet, smiling civility which is so rarely to be found in Paris.

At any rate, one night when we dropped in for dinner I noticed that at a conspicuously well set table, almost in the center of the room, a rather strange-looking couple had established itself.

That is to say, the woman was certainly a total stranger, while the young man who sat facing her—a boy of sixteen or seventeen at the very most—seemed vaguely familiar to me; but it was not until after our soup course had been served that I finally managed to decipher his true identity. He was undoubtedly our neighborhood coal dealer's eldest son, but he was so elaborately smartened up on that particular evening that I could hardly believe it was the same boy.

His lady, who was constantly eyeing him with a certain proprietary demureness, was surely many years his senior and was, without any possibility of error, quite obviously a prostitute.

Now, please, let me clarify this seemingly cruel categorical pronouncement and permit me to elucidate it in terms of its exact sociological context. This female companion of Maurice's (that was the boy's name) was extremely pretty and unobtrusively well mannered, and, what's more, she was rather smartly but not too lavishly decked out for the occasion; her black suit and dark-green toque with its half veil would have seemed perfectly appropriate on any other well-dressed woman in the room. She ate and drank with evident relish but with the modest decorum one generally associates with orderly domestic circumstances.

And yet I knew with absolute certainly that she was a professional prostitute because she had lacquered her nails with some sort of highly iridescent fluid and was wearing noticeably elaborate facial makeup. No woman of the French petty bourgeoisie would, under any circumstances, have worn such makeup, at least not during the period of time which is here under discussion. I'm talking about the year 1937, and I think that this state of affairs held true even until shortly after the close of the Second World War.

So, as I've been telling you, there they sat, almost in the middle of the room, and all around them the local tradesmen and their wives were munching away at their veal cutlets and their lamb vinaigrette, and these simple delicacies were accompanied by various appropriate wines, as well as by crisp seasonal salads and fruits not too terribly prepossessing in their appearance, but which, nevertheless, gave off an unbelievably rich and appetizing fragrance.

Now, get this straight!

Everybody in that restaurant knew perfectly well that Maurice, the coal dealer's eldest son, was about to have his first real sexual experience that very night. It was all so patently obvious that, somehow, I couldn't resist the notion that even the half dozen children sitting all around us must have been completely aware of the true state of things.

And yet, let me say to the eternal glory of that little gathering assembled in that Parisian cooky-nooky, that nobody in that room, either by word or by gesture, gave the slightest outward sign that anything untoward was about to happen. There was, I will admit, a certain submerged feeling of festiveness about the place. Indeed, an almost tangible vibration of communal goodwill seemed to emanate from that small gathering of average folk, and only very rarely was I able to catch some busily masticating matron casting a furtively appraising, sideward glance in Maurice's direction. However, I must insist that these subtle visual reconnoiterings were completely bereft of even the slightest contamination of prurience.

Later, while we were having our desserts, I discreetly consulted our waiter, whose name was Hilaire, about Maurice's impending splash into manhood. Since Hilaire knew a little English, we conducted our soft-spoken dialogue in that language.

"Yes," he said, "Maurice is going to be seventeen in a few months, and he has really been pretty restless of late. He is a very nice boy and very devoted to his family. He is doing all the paper work for his father now, and he is certainly a great help to him."

And that was that.

I could just imagine it all. I could imagine Maurice's mother at some time during the past few weeks complaining to the old man that the boy seemed unusually irritable and most uncharacteristically short-tempered toward everyone and saying that it might perhaps be a good notion to speak to the local padre about him. I could also easily guess the father's reaction to this suggestion and the knowing, fugitive smile that must have lurked about his grizzled mustache as he patted his wife reassuringly on the back.

"It will be quite all right, Marguerite," he had probably said to her. "I think I know what is wrong with the boy. He is a very good lad, and I think all he really needs is just a little holiday. That is all."

I could also conjecture how, later on, Papa had quietly given his son three hundred francs, had playfully pinched him on the cheek and said to him: "Amuse yourself a little, my boy. It is spring and you are young only once."

I'd be willing to bet my neck that there was no more to it than that. The rest, a French boy would easily know how to manage for himself. And since there was nothing dirty or underhanded in what was about to happen, Maurice saw no reason for being furtive about his actions, and so he had naturally brought his lady of the evening to the restaurant of his own neighborhood. Indeed, I don't think it was too farfetched to imagine that he would finally take her to the little Hotel Seville that was located close by, right around the corner from his home.

When Maurice and his companion were nearly done with their meal, the waiter suddenly approached their table and presented them with a fresh bottle of wine, which nestled luxuriously in a napkin-draped basket.

Maurice looked at the waiter in evident surprise, upon which Hilaire pointed significantly to the far side of the room and said, "M. Robillet sends you this bottle with his compliments and hopes you will drink to his health."

Maurice rose from his chair as M. Robillet, a retired police official, half rose from *his*, and after the cork had been cleanly drawn the two men smilingly lifted their glasses toward each other and drank bottoms up. The lady at the table had also taken a modest sip, and when Robillet was finished wiping his mustache he held up a freshly filled glass and said: "Good hunting, my boy!"

No more than that.

Maurice and his companion stayed long enough to finish half their wine, and I noticed that Hilaire carefully wrapped up the bottle and placed it in the pocket of the young man's overcoat, which was hanging on a clothes rack right near the cash desk.

At last they rose to leave. In the doorway Maurice turned around and bowed to the assembled company, which responded by presenting faces of unanimously jovial encouragement. His lady friend gave a smallish nod in the general direction of M. Robillet, and, after she had straightened out her escort's muffler with a gesture of almost maternal concern and protectiveness, they finally stepped, arm in arm, out into the soft Parisian night.

Well, maybe you don't care too much for this story. Maybe you are one of those lucky ones whose first sexual experience happened under idyllic circumstances—on a moonlit night somewhere, in a leaf-shadowed arbor, on moss-covered turf, while the nightingales were singing their little hearts out in the swoon-inducing fragrance of the nearby jasmine bushes. It may even be that the angel you were involved with was your childhood sweetheart, whose father owned a flock of oil wells and whose mother thought you'd make just about as ideal a son-in-law as she was ever likely to find.

I said *Maybe!*—didn't I?

CHAPTER FIVE

F OR A VERY little while I believed that the rich had all
of the properly authorized and *un*authorized fun in the world.
I'd see their flabby, overly barbered faces in the newspapers and
magazines and I would observe, from my small vantage point of
constantly shifting resources, as they went yachting along the
Mediterranean coast on their exotically bibulous excursions into
seemingly inevitable serendipity.

I'd see their improbably tinted, tight-bottomed women, their
various seasonably appropriate homes, which, I must admit, often
looked like swank waiting rooms in long-deserted railroad sta-
tions; I'd scan the faces of their self-sufficient, multiple-mothered
children, and I was convinced that a few lucky stiffs had really
managed to latch on to the tail of at least perpetual repose, if not
consistently high-pitched ecstasy.

They also had a few troubles; I knew all about that too. But if anybody told me that wealthy people were unhappy most of the time, I'd smile a little knowing smile, because I was certain that some well-paid public-relations manipulators had deliberately set that notion into motion so that the restless rest of us wouldn't become *too* fretful when their glittering Rolls-Royces splattered our reversible topcoats as they went speeding heedlessly past us on the way to their glorious assignations.

Well, I've gotten to know quite a pack of rich people, rather intimately, too, and I must say that most of them have a pretty terrible time of it. When I say "Rich People," I don't mean the financial wizards who think they've cornered the stock market for a couple of months and who, a year or two later, are out looking for jobs as night watchmen or who have to run off on one-way tickets to Brazil to think things over for a while. I mean the members of the top financial echelons, the ones who are so loaded with loot that no matter what they or their silly children might possibly do, they could never manage to get rid of it all in just one lifetime.

I can truthfully say to you that I've observed quite a few of these creatures over protracted periods of time, both here and abroad, and that most of their waking hours are spent in fighting off an all-pervading state of absolutely relentless boredom. The things they contrive with so much elaboration, things which seem so eccentric to the rest of us, are merely small outward manifestations of a desperate effort to come to terms with a constantly increasing inner vacuity.

Dear Moss Hart once said to me, "The rich get wrinkles from laughing." He was most grievously mistaken. The rich get wrinkles from *yawning*.

In short, somebody, somewhere, has certainly sold us a big, fat lie about the consolations inherent in great wealth and the ultimate comforts to be derived from absolute financial security. Come to think of it, hardly anybody (I mean anybody we're liable to pay any attention to) ever seems to take the trouble to wise us up about this state of affairs. I know the Bible has quite a lot

35

to say on this subject and says it repeatedly, too, but unfortunately we don't much go to the Bible when we want guidance for our daily life.

The Bible impinges on our awareness, if at all, mostly on Sundays, and that is generally when we also meet the minister or the padre or the rabbi. These men have special roles to fulfill in our society, and we are certainly aware of it. At the same time, we can't help noticing that they are, by and large, a well-fed lot; that they wear good clothes, drive shining, late-model automobiles—and we take it for granted that their comfortably furnished homes possess well-stocked larders in which the abundance of the land and the richness of the vineyard are fully manifest. It is possible that some of us may even conjecture them to be suffering in the *spirit*—since as far as the *flesh* is concerned they seem obviously to be doing quite well.

Don't you worry: we don't begrudge them a thing. After all, we accept tennis pros and golf pros, and as far as we're concerned these gentlemen of the cloth are just religious pros. And that's about the size of it. We do consult them on certain unavoidable occasions, and, what's more, we are hardly ever completely at ease when we have reason to approach them about something personal. The basic cause for this is not that too many of us are suffering from hagiophobia (which means the unreasonable dread of sacred persons) but, rather, that most of us, during our rare contacts with these special creatures, have a strong tendency to suspect that either *they*, or *we*, or perhaps the whole mixed-up lot of us, are just a bunch of hopelessly compulsive playactors.

I think it was a great deal simpler in the past—the long-gone past, I mean. But after Copernicus and Galileo and Newton and Darwin and Einstein, people in nearly all walks of life had to revamp their acts, and I'm convinced that most of the professional religious in our midst ought to overhaul their attitudes and activities, too.

It may indeed have come to pass that their unctuous supervision of community bingo games no longer brings a lump of real reverence to anybody's esophagus.

Let's face it: we've seen some overwhelming changes take place in our time, and nothing is ever going to be quite the same as it was.

I know there are quite a number of good and even holy men still abroad in the world today. Luckily, the earth never lacked for saints and sages who cherished the welfare of humanity and the peace of their own souls above all other things. I am aware that many of them became those white, shining candles which often guided stumbling mankind through the years of its darkest travails. I have nothing but due praise for those nobly dedicated ones who are *still* prepared to immolate themselves on the altar of their unwavering faith that man is truly redeemable.

I myself believe this with all my heart.

That is why I get so sore about all this waste of time and effort to achieve a quick beatitude by means of things which can be purchased on credit in any nearby department store.

Of course, it may have occurred to you that I'm just jabbering along like this merely to please myself; that, actually, not very many people are really anxious to be so filthily rich as I'm pretending.

Well, I did gather something tangible out of those forty thousand letters that came to me quite unbidden, and I can synthesize my findings for you very simply by informing you that what most people want out of life is just a couple of cars, a reasonably sized Chris-Craft (a raised-deck cruiser), a modest town house, and maybe a little country place with a few acres of green around it (just to get away from all the hustle-bustle once in a while). No cattle, you understand; just some cows to give milk for the family and perhaps a couple of horses and some ponies for the children when the weather is nice. And that's about it. Nothing extravagant, you see; only a few of the simple pleasures and amenities of modern life.

Don't laugh! That paragraph almost completely encompasses the dominant *American Dream*.

That's what makes me so sick about it.

Think of all the great human beings who have lived and left

us a glorious record of their strivings and accomplishments on this earth. Not one of them settled for as little as you are willing to settle for right now. The names that fill our history books, the names that crowd the worthwhile shelves of our libraries are the names of men and women who seem to me nowadays as if they had been the inhabitants of another planet. Of course, we are not all destined to enrich the sum total of human knowledge or to engrave our initials in the golden bark on the tree of noble achievement; but our children, at least, ought to grow up in an atmosphere where the *True*, the *Good* and the *Beautiful* have a holy corner to themselves—and where *Wisdom* and *Learning* stand higher than the tinseled plateau on which a Cadillac is glitteringly enshrined as your family's most exalted aspiration.

That's why I say, "To hell with *Outer Space!*" (For the moment.) I am completely nauseated by our plans to land on the moon. I want to launch exploratory rockets to discover the miracles of *Inner Space* and perhaps to add some altogether new dimensions to man's capacity for feeling.

You can see that despite my superficial sophistication I'm really corny as hell. I still believe that man is somehow improvable. I don't care for him to take deadly microbes and viruses up to Venus and to Neptune, and I would much rather have him start to use those eight-tenths of his brain which still lie completely idle in most of us. Maybe science could discover some simple way by which we might absorb the seeds of altruism along with our mother's milk. It certainly seems worth trying, even if nobody is experimenting along those lines at all.

Of course, what riles me most is that the majority of our great efforts are bent toward goals whose final effects might result in the total annihilation of all of us.

Now please don't bother bringing up the Russians. When I despair of mankind, I certainly don't mean to exempt the Russians.

So, save your breath.

I also realize that I'm beginning to bore you, friends; nevertheless, let me say quickly that at this moment of our national existence the majority of my countrymen seem to be absolutely stupefied by the ceaseless glutting of their multifarious appetites. I think you can see for yourself that this enormous surfeit of comforts has certainly failed to give anybody *you* know any sort of lasting satisfaction.

I don't want people to forgo the decent physical advantages which modern life provides so abundantly. I just don't want us to be enslaved by a lot of trashy gadgets and to set our hearts (and the hearts of our children) on the acquisition of frivolous status symbols whose built-in, automatic deterioration conditions us for lifelong servitude to the merest trivia of existence.

I'm not the only one who feels all this so keenly. Lots of people, some of them very ordinary people scattered all over the land, are made profoundly uneasy by the fact that too many of us achieve personal identity only through the things we *own;* that much too many of us have set ourselves goals which promise to provide us with no satisfaction beyond a state of well-fed survival surrounded by a lot of obsolescent junk.

Good fodder and a warm stable were the common graces which a decent householder always tried to furnish for his useful, domestic animals.

They were never enough to appease the expectations of the human soul, and I profoundly pity anyone who refuses the Gift of Life only because he prefers to continue the comfortable, quasi intrauterine existence which was once, of necessity, provided for him, during his period of gestation, inside his mother's womb.

Indeed, I believe it is terribly depressing to live in a time in which a thing is not properly hallowed even in a religious sense until it has managed to achieve the accolade of popular success.

I'm afraid that a good many of us, upon rising to our labors each morning, ought to revise the ancient prayer and say, "O Lord, *forgive* us this day our daily bread!"

CHAPTER SIX

O NE DAY Oliver St. John Gogarty, the Irish physician-author who was the original of Buck Mulligan in *Ulysses*, said to me, "Probably the easiest thing in the world is to become a widely known success. All you have to do is stand with a shining red apple in your mouth on some busy street corner, and before you know it you've become a famous landmark. Of course, the trick is to stand there *long enough!*"

He was referring to the worldwide fame which had come so belatedly to James Joyce, because Mr. Gogarty was firmly convinced that *Ulysses* was just a gargantuan hoax which some shrewdly manipulative literary critics had successfully pulled off on the rest of us.

That wasn't the only thing Mr. Gogarty happened to be wrong about. Actually, I believe that *Ulysses* is the greatest comic masterpiece of all time, and I rate it superior to everything penned by Aristophanes or Rabelais—and, in my estimation, it outranks *The*

Satyricon, Don Quixote, Gil Blas, Candide, Guzmán de Alfa-rache, Simplicius Simplicissimus, and even *Tyll Eulenspiegel.* About the only book that I can recall that has given me almost as much delight is *Huckleberry Finn.*

As for the notion that it is an absolute cinch to become a great success through sheer persistence alone—well, I don't think that such a niggling estimate, with its reflection on Joyce's great achievement, really merits any rejoinder at all.

It stands to reason that *success* means different things to different people. It is surely no accident that almost all professional boxers as well as bullfighters have had their origins in the slums of cities. From the urinous crevice of an industrial town the shortest road to success leads almost inevitably to the *Mafia* or to the prize ring. Very frequently they amount to one and the same thing. This also explains a good deal about the later conduct of some of the successful practitioners in the boxing world when they finally do strike it rich. They act like boozed-up sailors out on a permanent spree, and since their special profession is largely monitored by criminal elements of all sorts, it is more than likely that even in the best instances they are eventually forced to retire with only a measly fraction of the money they had actually earned. Quite often they even end up as pathetic, punch-drunk mendicants, disdained by the very people who had for years crudely and heartlessly exploited their agonizing labors. That's *one* kind of success.

Then, of course, there are the few lucky girls in each quickly passing generation who, through the aegis of some precociously assertive mammary glands, coupled to tantalizingly provocative posteriors, happen to achieve wide notoriety by landing in a well-paid or, perhaps, only well-publicized niche provided within the elastic periphery of show business. That their subsequent careers add up to a series of scandalous episodes, interspersed with brief tableaux out of some elaborately vulgarized marital cha-rades, has never yet managed to discourage the more likely look-ing young females of the land from entering into fierce compe-tition to attain this particular form of gutter-stained apotheosis.

41

Indeed, in a republic like ours, where there is no established aristocracy (excepting the aristocracy of money), the seemingly most accessible goals have been established upon those tawdry pinnacles of sensationalism whereon the venial manipulators of public attention have been best able to focus the limelight of their own most sordid self-interest.

To be a success on these terms means that you add, automatically, to the extremely revolting image of the United States which has already been so damagingly projected to a great many foreign countries. I think that during the past decade our most famous movie stars have managed to cast more doubt upon our reputations as serious human beings struggling to maintain an honorable equilibrium in a bitterly troubled world than any number of blundering politicians could possibly have done, even during the most depressing interludes of our sometimes rather ineptly chaperoned foreign policy.

What depresses me most is that the grotesque behavior of some of these movie morons has had a definitely deleterious effect on the thought patterns of a lot of impressionable youngsters. A great many others who really ought to know better have also had their long-established life values distorted due, I believe, to the extraordinary amount of tolerance and even obvious envy with which large segments of our public seem to regard the vertiginous cavortings of some of these monstrously overpaid mental and emotional derelicts.

You see, a goodly number of Hollywood nitwits are constantly occupied in creating an hysterical effect of liveliness about themselves, and the reason they go on doing this is because they don't want you to suspect that they are really quite dead. It certainly seems to work for them, too. Only a very few sourpusses like myself can clearly perceive that the whole lot of them have been only rather expensively embalmed and are doing a marathon *danse macabre* in partnership with some equally moribund newspaper reporters.

That these antihuman proceedings have a bad influence all around is observable even in my special circle of acquaintance.

I know playwrights and novelists who do their damnedest to behave like typical movie stars; who build houses which they abandon when they are half completed; who fly to Lisbon for a weekend, to bring back a special bottle of *Strega;* and who ask their bed-rabbit secretaries to have them paged at a hotel in Tanganyika, where they've gone especially to make a fourth hand at bridge.

There is more of this going on than you imagine. I suppose it *is* rather tough to keep all your marbles straight when you have quite a bit of money on hand and you know that the government is going to grab most of it anyway. It has one rather fortunate result, all the same: it keeps most of these dunderheads out of the country, and you don't have to listen to any of their vapid chitchat unless you are ass enough to read about their frantic proceedings in the gossip columns of the daily papers.

Of course, when I hear that men and women who, at one time or another, have somehow managed to do some halfway decent work have also landed on the greasy chute that leads to the international nightclub circuit, it always depresses me for a couple of hours.

I like to think that members of the rather select freemasonry of the *actually alive* in this world have installed, somewhere in their psychic organisms, certain automatically self-regulating gyroscopes which keep them forever beautifully in balance with the creative harmony of the universe.

But in many ways I am quite well content.

I know that Isak Dinesen* is sitting at her desk in her bird

* Isak Dinesen (Karen Blixen) and e. e. cummings died shortly after my manuscript was completed.

She always seemed to me like one of those ancient wise women who used to tell their fabulous tales around communal firesides while their enraptured listeners sat in spellbound silence all around them.

I had had this image of her long before I came to know her personally, and when this blessed meeting finally occurred, it only helped to strengthen this preconceived pattern in my mind.

In a time of the most sterile artistic experimentation, her work remains a meaningful distillate of human joy and suffering as rendered by a personality of the most astonishing poetic endowments.

A great number of those who live by their wits are only too glad to acknowl-

sanctuary in Denmark and quietly plotting her next story, that
e. e. cummings* is probably correcting proofs on his next book
of poems, and that Marianne Moore, in a walk-up flat in Brook-
lyn, remains a true and faithful vestal to her highly exacting muse.
I'm also sure that Henry Miller is ensconced out on his peninsula
in the Pacific Ocean, writing and painting for no man's approval
except his own, and that in his spare time he swaps stories with
people who can't help loving him because sanity is his greatest
product!

I could name lots of others who use their rich faculties to ennoble a barren time; I have only mentioned these few because I
have either seen them or have had word from them in the very
recent past.

I can tell you a few things about *my* own particular success
during the past few years. It has made it possible for me to meet,
or at least to reach out to, a great many people whom I have esteemed in my heart for a long time and who were only waiting
for a sign from me so they could give me a friendly nod of recognition and reassurance.

That's the *big plus* of the whole deal, if you want to know the
truth!

It may also be that you are quite unaware of the fact that I

---

edge their indebtedness to her, and thousands upon untold thousands have
benefited by her miraculous gift of almost clairvoyant perceptiveness.

She was, in the truest sense of the term, a noble human being, and her art,
fortunately for all of us, was a genuine extension of the unique character traits
that marked her whole existence.

I find it absolutely shattering to be compelled to speak about her in the past
tense, and the only consolation left to me is the knowledge that the qualities that
so distinguished her are exquisitely enshrined in the literary legacy which she
has left, not only to us, but to endless generations still to be born.

---

* e.e. cummings, the joyous human being who celebrated *live* man with unim-
paired poetic fervor all throughout the years of his life, is now gone from us.
He was the special minnesinger of April, and in a time of emotional stultifica-
tion, the loss of him is most difficult to bear. We can see in his work that all the
seven good fairies were present at his birth, and those of us who knew and
cherished him are, indeed, greatly diminished by his death.

have been acting like a great success for a long, long time. Excepting only that one grim decade of my very grave illness, I always lived in pleasant homes, with people who loved me and whom I loved in turn. My walls were always decorated by fine pictures and African masks, while my shelves were pleasantly burdened by books containing the world's greatest literature. My doors were hospitably open during all hours of the day and even most of the night, on the bare chance that a human being who had successfully emerged out of the dark womb of ancient prejudice and superstition and had finally learned to think for himself without fear or misgivings *might have something significant to say to me.*

It didn't happen often. But it *did* happen, once in a while. It hardly *ever* happens nowadays.

I know why, too. The truthtellers have all died or become old and are well known to me.

Most of the others who come to my door just want to sell me something. I'm really not in the market for much.

When I was young I enjoyed driving high-speed cars, and I even owned a couple of summer homes, at various times, when my children were still small. Nowadays I wouldn't know what to do with things as extraneous as that.

In my closet there hang three suits (all of them black), half a dozen gray shirts, two dozen gray bow ties, three pairs of shoes (all black), and my wife and I have furnished an apartment in which the greatest luxury items are some large, handwoven Chinese and Spanish floor rugs, which we have owned for quite a long time.

I can tell you that my life, since my truly remarkable book sales began, has changed only in manner and not at all in its basic substance. I now live in a house that has an elevator, since the climbing of many stairs has become a real hardship for me. I also have a little more room to walk around in, and it is my common habit to turn down practically every sort of job which is offered to me.

This often happened in the past, too, although we sometimes needed the money pretty badly. You see, it has been my lifelong habit to reject any type of work which I felt would represent a

45

criminal waste of my time. After all, I only had this one, irreplaceable existence to eke out with, and I certainly couldn't afford to treat my precious days as if they were just so much dirty confetti.

No matter what my circumstances were, I never made any drawings to illustrate any of the Sears Roebuck catalogues, for instance, although, on several occasions such jobs were offered to me and I was almost stone-broke when these great opportunities happened to come my way.

I was actually never too sure what a great opportunity really consisted of. Very often I couldn't help feeling that it was probably nothing more than just an enormous, carelessly exposed septic tank.

My social life has shrunk down quite a bit, too, since I no longer have to consort with any of my merely rich contemporaries.

This is certainly a relief.

Years ago I used to labor under the youthful delusion that people who were well-heeled might be overwhelmingly inclined to patronize a talented painter. It was very foolish of me and turned out to be a horrible waste of time. It is also due to this sadly futile period of my life that I owe a good many of my current ailments.

You must understand that, for quite a long while, I was considered a very promising young man. Later on, I naturally became a very promising *middle-aged* man. Basically, none of this was true, because I've had many real successes in my life and quite a few of those *shmucks* who patronized me were actually in no position to consider me a failure. I was often very fortunately involved with some extremely beautiful women; I always got up or went to sleep whenever I felt like it; and, most important of all, I was *never* owned by my possessions. I traveled widely in many lands, and I always had time to read and to talk, to my heart's content, with anyone who had achieved a reasonably civilized state of maturity.

However, as I've already confessed to you, my biggest piece

of idiocy was the ridiculous notion that the rich cared anything at all about art. In pursuit of this phantasmagoria, I used to go quite frequently to their homes to take late dinner with them, and it was during these hideously depressing nocturnal sessions that I, very effectively, managed to ruin my stomach, my liver, my kidneys, and even my poor and blameless pancreas. You see, I'd fallen into the unfortunate habit of wolfing down my food as quickly as possible; not because I was hungry—which I was *not* —but because I wanted to get through with my meals in a hurry so that I would be in the best strategic position to take complete charge of the conversation.

I don't mean that I wanted to monopolize all the talk in those gastronomical mortuaries. I simply wanted to make sure that the locutional stream, whose gushing impulses were somewhat re-strained by the delaying processes of food ingestion, would not, finally, be compelled to carry a too-deadly load of just boring verbal driftwood. I had to use all of my not inconsiderable skill and cunning to hastily quarantine all references to current golf scores and to elaborately involved business shenanigans and to forestall with a perfect frenzy of concentrated inventiveness all possible quotations from the mouths of various grotesquely over-rated nephews, nieces, and grandchildren.

Believe me, it was a tough job.

It often happened that the rest of the company was still fiddling with the roast while I was already finishing off my dessert. I gen-erally managed to get very snappy table service by pretending that a tremendously significant, long-distance phone call was about to change the whole course of my life and was certainly destined to tear me, momentarily, away from this scintillating assemblage of wit, beauty, charm, and affluence.

Although such phone calls never materialized, nobody, as far as I can recall, ever seemed to take the slightest notice of these omis-sions. You can't really blame them, either. After three prepara-tory cocktails, a nine-course dinner (each course accompanied by some suitable tipple) followed by several cups of coffee, and, finally, the whole business topped off by some highly aromatic *liqueurs*, you may well believe that the world's problems, even the most acute ones, had a tendency to be suffused by a rather benign haze.

And that is how it fortunately came about that the discrepancies of my own paltry existence were all happily lost sight of in the obliterating fogs of everyone's postprandial stupefaction.

CHAPTER SEVEN

ALTHOUGH I HAVE for quite a while been afflicted by a variety of physical ailments, I have hardly ever suffered from sleeplessness. As a matter of fact, I can truthfully say that on the very few occasions in the past when I did fall under what is commonly considered the blight of insomnia I often rather welcomed these additional spells of wakefulness because they gave me a chance to do a little uninterrupted analytical thinking, for which the active noonday hours rarely allowed me sufficient repose.

I remember now that sometimes during those wakeful spells nearly twenty-five years ago the most frequently recurring topic for my nocturnal ruminations used to be the constantly engrossing question whether European women were, by and large, more satisfactory partners for matrimony than their coequals on this side of the Atlantic.

I recall very clearly that I had really few doubts or misgivings on this problem at that time because it seemed patently obvious to me that American wives still had a great deal to learn from their domesticated sisters in the old country.

Let me tell you at once that the passing years have brought a considerable alteration in my opinions on this subject, and nowadays when I again come to appraise this fascinating proposition, perpendicularly, in broad daylight, I cannot resist the conclusion that quite a number of married ladies on this side of the water have indeed little to learn and even something to teach to almost all the other women of the modern world.

I will presently tell you about my change of heart.

Of course, I had decided long ago, during my midnight meanderings among these recondite subjects, that the ideal matings on this globe of ours certainly take place among the dragonflies, who meet and consummate their ultimate communion in midair. We who are a good deal more circumscribed in fulfilling our romantic commitments are compelled to make peace with our earthbound condition and must submit to gravity in more ways than one. Another thing: the very briefness of an insect's life automatically guarantees that the partners in a matrimonial duet shall never live long enough to suffer even the most primary of postnuptial disillusionments.

The next most satisfactory marriages surely take place among the Eskimos. When I say "Eskimos," I don't mean the sadly debauched creatures who wear Japanese Mother Hubbards and fiber-glass sport slacks; I mean the honest-to-goodness articles who live on raw seal and who still build igloos made out of real ice.

I just don't believe there ever could be a bad Eskimo wife—or husband either, for that matter—because if they are unfit to tackle their jobs, they are automatically condemned to instant extinction. Remember, they have no government of any kind and each family reigns supreme over its own destiny. Every member of each small clan is responsible not only for himself but also for the fate of the entire unit.

The husband provides the food, builds the home, takes care of his dogs and hunting gear, and teaches his sons the minutely artful skills of survival under stone-age conditions.

The mother chews the family boots (to keep them supple), sews the garments, looks after the fuel, and teaches her daughters to walk with pigeon-toed propriety in her own dutiful footsteps.

Can you imagine an Eskimo woman leaning back some sub-zero evening and saying to her husband, "Listen, Oomook, I've got a pretty bad toothache coming on; I don't think it would exactly kill you if you chewed your own damned boots for a change."

Can you *really* imagine such a thing?

I certainly can't.

But let us get back and investigate our more temperately zoned conditions a little farther.

First of all, I must confess at once that, in any large-scale generalization of this sort, one is bound to override quite a number of palpable exceptions which happen to violate one's own didactic predilections. I insist, however, that despite these occasional cases of opposing merit, which may easily come to anyone's mind, I am, at this moment, very much in the mood of proving the substantial accuracy of my own findings, and, what is more, I am prepared to defend them to the very last drop of my ink.

Curiously enough, even a quarter of a century ago, whenever I thought about Europe in its contextual reference to prospective brides, I invariably had reference to the continental slab of land which largely marks off this specific geographic sector and I never under any circumstances included England in my calculations at all. Actually, the reason for this almost instinctive oversight was very simple: it was my lifelong habit to couple English and American women in the identical framework of my prejudices, because I was somehow convinced that the ladies of these countries were emotionally equally detached, if not actually frigid, in their more intimate relationships with men.

The notion was definitely abroad in the world that they were really not much fun to sleep with, that most Anglo-Saxon gals thought of sex as a peculiarly male affliction, to the effects of which a dutiful wife suffered herself to submit from time to time while always remembering not to display any emotions beyond a state of patient endurance. Actual encouragement along these lines was considered the peculiar prerogative of prostitutes.

This surely spelled irrevocable disaster for any marriage which I cared to envisage, and since the basic groundwork for my prejudices was laid in Austria, I can assure you that this is exactly how most of the Central European men of my acquaintance felt about this matter.

In the course of my life I also came to know quite a number of so-called Caucasian men who, for various highly involved reasons, had a distinct preference for Asian women as prospective marriage partners. Let me say at once that I considered such men and their peculiar predispositions beyond the pale of my own serious interests. Purdah, in any form, had always seemed to me rather odious and degrading to everyone involved with it, because I was convinced that no man with any self-esteem would ever want his wife to live behind the veil or to sit below the salt.

In short, I always thought of myself as a modern man, in the truly best sense of that word. I frankly confess to you that I have never really enjoyed myself in the locker rooms of country clubs, and I have always preferred social setups in which at least a few women were present as social equals. In fact, the sentence "Let us join the ladies" has all through my life filled me with a sense of pleasant expectancy, which is still quite undiminished at the age of sixty-two. I am offering you these perhaps trivial personal asides merely to help orient you on my own special attitudes toward the opposite sex and to furnish you with a shadowy projection of my instinctive posture in this eternal man-woman business.

Now then, after two world wars which scattered citizens of this country all over the globe and brought women into those offices and factories where only their fathers and brothers had once held tangible authority, it was no longer possible to pay anything but the most perfunctory lip service to a great many

Victorian concepts which had influenced a good deal of our behavior in the past.

The sexual emancipation had come upon us in a sudden blast, and we can now see that this was indeed one of the very few real benefits that accrued to us from these world-shaking disasters. I think it was all for the best. I personally am enormously pleased by the free use of all the new human prerogatives which have come to the women of this country in recent years.

Incidentally, I think I had better clarify what I mean when I say "European women" or "American women." I specifically *don't* mean ladies of the aristocracy (both lineal and financial), and I wish to exempt also, and forever, all women who are successfully connected with any aspect of the theatrical world. After all, as someone once very aptly remarked, "These people, all too often, live like anarchists under police protection." This is only too true, and the special conditions which prevail in those highly peculiar spheres can hardly apply as standard measuring units for the rest of mankind. When I say *men* or *women*, I mean members of the middle or upper-middle class, among whom I myself was raised and with whose lives I have been thoroughly familiar throughout the years.

My aunts and female cousins in Austria, for instance, passed their youth under conditions of such exigent chaperonage that it very frequently bordered on the Spanish duenna system. Even so, it was obvious to me that these young females, preparing themselves for a life of fruitful domesticity under the strictest imaginable family surveillance, were, nevertheless, infinitely better prepared to assume their oncoming responsibilities as wives than most of their transatlantic sisters whom I later came to know in the United States. These European girls had a good deal less freedom, but what they did have in abundance was *a well-established routine for proper wifehood*. They could see by the examples of their mothers and married sisters that women had highly complicated roles to fulfill, roles which equipped the participants with proper attitudes and devices to meet the most seemingly unexpected, and even disastrous, happenstances. Of course, the girls of my adolescence in Vienna somehow or other learned to condone, quite early, the double standard of morality prevalent during those years, and they were well aware of the frightening possibility that their men *might*, at some time or another, become involved in extramarital diversions with other women. While this was certainly deplored and even officially considered scandalous and frowned upon by all respectable people, the wife realized that, beyond all other considerations, her most important responsibility was to keep the family intact, come hell or high water.

You will say that this is utterly shameful, and that it represents a humiliating, unendurable concession on the wife's part, and that it is something that certainly ought not to be tolerated in civilized society. What's more—I quite agree with you.

At the same time, I often observed that by their evident moral superiority these injured women managed automatically to gain a deadly stranglehold on the soiled consciences of their erring life partners. And they *were* life partners, too: that's the point I'd like you to keep in mind.

Another thing: because of the prevailing mores of the time, a married woman was compelled to be constantly in competition with the alarming image of an ever-possible mistress, and in consequence of this disquieting eventuality she became enormously adroit in employing *all* of her fascinating gender endowments.

She learned that to be a pleasing paramour was an important pivotal point in her relationship with her man, and she accepted this situation unequivocally since no one had warned her or alarmed her into thinking that there was anything sinful about this. Actually, the majority of them led happily fulfilled sex lives, in the course of which they also quite naturally acquired many small but significant skills, which bind a man more certainly to his own bedside than all the hand-monogrammed, sachet-reeking pillow slips in the world.

It certainly had *some* good results.

There were very few divorces.

You may well say that any marriage with such quasi-oriental overtones isn't worth an old jar of rancid peanut butter, and you may very well be in the right. What interests me enormously, however, is that a young American wife of that same era, faced with her own unforeseeable matrimonial problems, had practically no fund of basic information with which to face such contingencies, beyond her possible capacity for turning out a batch of passable root-beer muffins. I daresay American husbands, even half a century ago, were far less likely to keep mistresses than their European counterparts; but the great error in the training of their wives lay in the grotesque assumption that it could *never* happen and that if it ever *did* happen, it could only happen among unnaturally depraved people—social derelicts, perhaps—and even *then* only among *foreigners*.

Just to keep the record straight, let me assure you that I don't wish to imply here that the European or South American woman's readiness to accept her husband's infidelity represents a basically indispensable attribute which goes for the making of a good wife. Nothing could be farther from my mind. I'll tell you what this *does* represent: it represents a ready recognition of possible human frailty which *might* have to be met with mature fortitude and even womanly forgiveness; it predicates an adult acceptance of a potentially fallible world. And I believe that this in its turn is bound to manifest itself with benign effects in an infinite number of ways relative to a good many lesser matters which are likely to arise between people in their day-to-day living.

At this point I am moved to consider how miraculous a free and democratic marriage can really be. Just think! Two total strangers come together and, as absolute equals, suddenly decide to mingle their passions, their aspirations and their confusions in an entirely new family pattern. Isn't it remarkable how often such a seemingly jeopardous undertaking works out satisfactorily for all concerned? Keep in mind also that these chronic optimists often come from totally different backgrounds and that they have decided to modify their identities only after the idealisms, the frustrations, and the dreams of childhood and adolescence have been temporarily muted *but by no means extinguished.*

I am certain, however, that the basic difference between the European women and their English and American prototypes was conditioned by the fact that the Anglo-Saxon ladies largely grew up and matured in societies which still wallowed in the backwash of an emotionally stultifying Puritanism.

That, I think, is the *real* crux of the matter.

And that is precisely why an American bride suddenly emerging into a constantly changing society, whose momentous alterations could actually be marked from day to day, finally had no really sustaining marriage pattern left to follow. With her ever-increasing freedoms, there came not only a long-overdue personal liberation but, unfortunately, also a certain vertigo of the soul. Her heart became a battlefield of conflicting social and sexual syndromes, and she was compelled to improvise on a part for which there was no written script and which certainly had no historical parallel. She saw only too clearly through a good many of the social hypocrisies which had kept her female forebears in harness, and only too frequently she had nowhere to turn for any trustworthy immediate guidance. She was often shrill and petulant, merely to cover her own bewilderment with her altogether novel condition.

She was like a golden Rapunzel who sometimes wanted to let down her hair, only to remember at the last moment that several weeks before she had had it all cut off to a mere boyish bob.

That is why some decades ago, when this condition first really came to a boil, I thought that her Austrian and French sisters would make far more desirable wives for any reasonably prudent bridegrooms.

I am happy to report that a good deal of this is no longer true. Some of the American women I know and have come to esteem are an altogether different breed. Of course, they tend to stumble, and many of them still fall; but, if they once have learned to command their psychic equilibriums, they are the most desirable marriage partners to be found in the world today. They are truly worthy of a man's esteem, because they come into matrimony as open-eyed partners who can freely bestow their emotional treasures without reservations and without undue misgivings.

I think that this state of affairs marks an entirely new epoch in the field of marriage. Remember that life even in ancient Greece and Rome was heavily overlaid with Asian influences. As far as I know, there was never a time in recorded history when so many women were free to find fulfillment as complete human beings in that rich creative partnership which can represent matrimony in our time.

The European woman of today is also slowly coming within hailing distance of a similar goal. And she seems to be in precisely the same state of social and emotional ferment that not so very long ago beset our American brides.

This might be the moment for me to tell you that I have personally observed that marriages between Europeans and Americans seem to carry a number of additional hazards for both participants to the venture and that it is certainly the better part of cautious valor not to intermarry unless you know these people for quite a long time. There are many complex causes for my state of mind, and one of the apparently most trifling hazards, which has recently again come to my attention, seems, nevertheless, to be quite effective in creating considerable irritation between the people involved.

You see, the European educational system is definitely more exacting and rigorous than ours. This is certainly true in all the grades below college level, and so it happens quite frequently that a Hollander or a German who is married to an American girl will sometimes quite inadvertently tend to display a certain amount of scholastic snobbery. This superiority can manifest itself in later life in nothing more tangible than some inaccurate quotations from the Latin classics or perhaps a few quite malapropos excerpts from an obscure troubadour poet. In any event, after a while the diminished bride may learn to resent these too frequently repeated public applications of literary poultices, and she may finally come to be completely exasperated by such exhibitions of a long-perished high-school precocity. I can most earnestly testify that these things actually do happen in our midst. I have witnessed not only the long-drawn-out provocations but, alas, I was also most unhappily present at some of the catastrophic denouements.

Another thing: an American girl who marries a Spanish or Portuguese gentleman is likely to discover that his loudly expressed sentiments on the equality of the sexes are actually substantiated by his belief in complete freedom for all women, excepting only his wife. After all, she doesn't really need freedom if she's got *him*. The lucky girl!

As for culture snobbery among European women, I think it is frequently even more pronounced than among their men and, in most instances, is founded on a basis of considerably less substantiable density. In several instances which I myself had occasion to verify, it consisted mostly of reminiscences on such subjects as self-expressive sessions at various dancing classes and long, dewy-eyed attendances at sundry European opera houses. On closer examination, I invariably discovered that most of these ladies had once done some sporadic reading among the better-known French and Russian novelists and a very few could even remember the general plot structures of these distinguished works. I noted particularly that there was a strong tendency among these girls to eke out their intellectual lapses with meaningful eye-rollings, gurglings and gaspings in varying keys and intensities, which demonstrations clearly indicated to the sympathetic initiate that their aesthetic recollections were just too much for words.

But not really.

Their American husbands could easily testify that there was seemingly no end to their capacities for total verbal recall on such significant subjects, for instance, as who has conducted *Wozzeck* every single season since they themselves had been itsy-bitsy little girls way back in the good old days in highly musical Bratislava.

But let me be just.

I have certainly known some European ladies who were great scholars and gifted artists, and two of them were even celebrated mathematicians. Such women hardly ever marry American men. Indeed, I have known them to commit themselves matrimonially with citizens of the United States only twice in nearly forty years, and the two brides in question were well past middle age when these nuptials occurred. You are, of course, free to deduce from this strictly personal statistic whatever happens to suit your own charming fancy.

Since I have no other charts or graphs to hand at this time, all I say is necessarily predicated on my own personal experiences (and prejudices, if you like), so I feel free to tell you that the most satisfactory wives I have met during the past forty-five years in this country seemed to have had their primary origins on farms. I very definitely don't mean *small towns*. I mean *real farms*. The explanation for this may actually be very simple, too. After all, a young girl raised amid the constant matings, couplings, and spawnings that are the daily affiliates to all forms of rural existence certainly doesn't have to be told anything about the basic facts of life. Heaven knows, human behavior is full of all sorts of inhibitions and irritating social pretenses, even among farmers' daughters; but there is a greater chance that among these few, at least, certain forms of ignorance and false prudery have been replaced by a healthy acceptance of a world whose rawest impacts were observed by them at an early age and from a front-row seat.

Apropos of learning about life, I am suddenly reminded of my cousin Amelia, back in Vienna, who talked to me, long after she was happily married, about the years of her own young girlhood in a strict Austrian convent.

"I think it is quite impossible to shelter anyone completely from the world," she told me. "I discovered when I was only fifteen years old that all over Europe, and certainly in our own country, there existed a custom of legalized prostitution."

"How did that happen?" I asked.

"Oh, I heard the head porter at the convent scolding one of our new gardeners for having visited such a sinful place, and as they were jawing away at each other I gathered a good deal of sinister information. The old porter talked warningly about the dangers of social diseases and all of the other hazards that beset a life of fleshly indulgence, and you can be sure that within less than an hour all of my schoolmates were as thoroughly familiar with all of the relevant details as I myself was."

Now please don't assume that I consider a knowledge of legal prostitution an important adjunct to a young girl's education.

What I do claim is that an awareness of even the most sordid aspects of reality will in the end do less harm than *total ignorance*. That goes for girls just as well as for boys.

Nowadays, with coeducation rampant all over the land, there is surely no longer any cause for fear that a young woman may remain indefinitely unaware of the most important problems relating to her maturity. Her sensible, protective parents will see to that. Mothers and daughters can certainly practice a healthful outspokenness, which would have been inconceivable half a century ago. As a matter of fact, I believe that most of the mothers of that time had really very little to tell their daughters, since for the majority of them the whole subject of sex was located way out of bounds, in Tabu-land, in which hazardous territory they themselves had to improvise their bitterly self-conscious attitudes from moment to moment.

A story which I think aptly demonstrates the general sexual climate of that time was told to me by a friend some thirty-five years ago down on New York's lower East Side. It seems that a young boy saw his father coming out of a brothel one afternoon and the youngster stepped up to his parent and proceeded to reproach him for his lecherous conduct.

"Please!" said the father. "Will you stop making such a racket? What is it you want me to do? You want me to bother your poor mother on such a hot day just on account of a couple of lousy dollars?!?"

Well, I'm certainly glad that those delightful times are finally over and done with and that women nowadays can accept the full joys and risks of their femininity in all their multifarious ramifications.

It surely makes for a better life for everybody involved.

It surely makes for better wives, for people like *me*.

Finally, as I told you before, the old guidelines for marriage which have obtained in Europe throughout the centuries are slowly giving way to a new order, too.

Indeed, it is my belief that the brides of France and Germany, Italy and Austria are now faced with the same bewildering problems that come in the wake of all newfound freedoms and that, just a few decades ago, so thoroughly confused the married ladies of this country.

Many of these foreign women are making a botch of it right now, just as a good number of our own young women did when the age-old shackles of superannuated and fetish-ridden matrimonial customs first fell from their own bright young limbs.

What it all finally comes down to is what sort of a wife a man really wants. This is a highly personal and minutely relative matter, of course. I can imagine some man, even nowadays, who might prefer to be mated to a docile, altogether uncritical woman with just enough arithmetic about her so she can be safely trusted behind the cash register; and perhaps what he wants above all may be a person who will approach his parents (particularly his mother) with an almost Chinese sense of family reverence. Who knows what sort of weird, atavistic strains are still rampant in the human psyche?

My own peculiar temperament makes me quite unfit to make proper allowances for this sort of emotional retardation; what is more, I don't have the slightest wish to proselytize among the heathen for a cause whose advantages must be obvious to anyone whose intellectual development has equipped him to live with full maturity among his equals.

Naturally, I have tackled this highly complicated problem and drawn my deductions about it on the basis of purely personal observation. I justify my conclusions by carefully reviewing in my mind the sundry marriages I have been familiar with over many years, and, also, I have given you the usufruct of my own experiences, particularly as they relate to my current connubial situation, which is an extremely fortunate one.

Margie and I have been married for ten years, which means that we have been together at least twice as long as any other couple that stepped up to the preacher just one decade ago. You see, I work at home and my wife and I are hardly ever out of each other's sight or hearing. Believe me, that's a *real* test of matrimony. So, when *I* talk about a happy marriage, I can assure you I really *know* what I'm talking about.

There is one thing that rather tends to get me down in our current society, and that is something that may eventually endanger the whole concept of matrimony as we have known it throughout the many, many generations. I'm referring, of course, to the indiscriminate sleeping around that is taking place among our present-day teen-agers, which is not just an American phenomenon at all. My European friends assure me that a real moral earthquake is shaking the Old Country and that the rate of illegitimacy on the other side is now at an all-time high.

I know for a fact—and this time I have troubled to consult all available statistics—that the conditions along these lines in the United States are even more alarming. If you consider that these highly shocking data are very definitely *understating* the case, since *statistics on abortions are not available at all*, then you will begin to understand why I am so profoundly uneasy about this whole mess.

Actually, I don't see why I should work myself into a tizzy whenever my mind happens to dwell on this subject, since I would certainly much rather spend my time with a talented, or at least an amusing, bastard than have myself be imposed upon by a —no matter how legitimately spawned—moron. But I'll gladly concede to you that there are some problems which agitate our world and in which my personal tolerances ought to have no weight whatever; and I think *this* is one of them. You see, I realize that a society conceived and predicated on principles like ours cannot possibly survive within the structure of its present framework if its legal and ethical basis is being jeopardized by a constantly rising tide of moral irresponsibility.

That's just common sense.

No matter how inefficient the family unit may superficially appear (to some philosophically detached Utopians), it has so far proven itself as the most effective shelter behind which the basic humanities have had the most abundant opportunities for flowering into beneficent enrichment of the whole community.

There can't be any argument about *that* either!

Well, if a great many of our nubile young women are manhandled and boy-fingered by every passing lout who happens to have some idle time at his disposal, then the future not only of matrimony but of all of civilized life as it has been practiced until now is, most emphatically, in a very shaky condition.

And that I *am* really worried about.

Among those forty thousand letters which the world addressed to me there were quite an alarming number from high-school and college girls who freely confessed to sexual involvements with extremely unsuitable and even dangerously unstable partners. The majority of them merely asked my advice about some particularly unfortunate affair that happened to be of grave anxiety to them at the moment of their writing, but, with astonishing candor, they all freely confessed to a whole series of indiscretions which had involved most of them even in their early childhoods. I was quite upset by these untidy avowals and could explain them to myself only by assuming that these unhappy girls had finally come to such a point of distraction and bewilderment with their situations that they were at last reduced to consulting an absolute stranger about some helpful suggestions which would lead them, if not to a solution, at least toward a reasonable justification for their untenable behavior.

Also—and this was indeed my saddest conclusion—I knew that quite a few of these girls had read all of my books and, perhaps, they hoped that, from my socially disengaged point of view, I might come to see their actions as wholesome signs of justifiable contempt against the mountainous hypocrisies which modern society has heaped up in such profusion all about us.

I answered each of these letters personally. I wrote with a heavy heart, too, because the role of moral moderator suits me very badly. But common humanity and sincere compassion prompted me to preach my litany of admonishments, and I plagiarized freely from the sayings and the writings of the great teachers of mankind, both dead and alive.

I quoted *myself* quite a bit, too. I pointed out to them that I had written, somewhere, that the dynamics of redemption were rooted in *self-discipline;* that nothing worth the having was ever attained by *self-indulgence;* and that no matter how anxious one might be to please others, it ought never to be done at the expense of one's own *self-esteem.*

You see, I said what has been said throughout the millennia in Ceylon, in Jerusalem, in Athens, in Rome, and in Schenectady. I pointed out to them that all but one of the civilizations which these names evoked had passed away because the common citizenry which had lived in the shadows of these exclamation points in the story of man's achievements had violated the sane and prudent sentences which had led up to such puissant punctuations.

I warned them not to be afraid of clichés, since it was very likely that the congenitally thoughtless and frivolous among us have come to disdain some of the pregnantly apt sayings of the past, chiefly because they happen to contain some particularly unpalatable truths.

And so on.

The worst of it is, almost all of these schoolgirls who wrote to me were, quite obviously, badly in need of psychiatric help. One could feel in their impulsively scribbled missives a desperate need for tenderness, and I am convinced that most of them had permitted themselves to be so injudiciously tampered with because they were chronically in search of approval—no matter whose, and no matter how obtained. They had started very early in life to cadge for acceptance and were prepared to make any sort of sacrifice to be received on equal terms, even by their patent inferiors.

I am describing an acutely wretched condition which exists all over the world today, and, believe me, even a comparative outsider like myself would gladly give some constructive help if any worthwhile program were ever to be activated for its amelioration.

In the meanwhile, heaven had better help *all of us!*

Whenever I happen to write of human behavior my mind invariably reverts to the "Sirfessor Klondike." He was a character who drifted about Greenwich Village nearly half a century ago, and I must say I always found him a most stimulating companion.

He was a graduate anthropologist, an honor student from a great university, who had somehow managed to booze himself into a pretty shabby state of professional bohemianism. He claimed to be only fifty-two years old when I first met him, but he certainly looked more like someone in his upper seventies. His real name was Carl Brennert, and when I once asked him what "Sirfessor" signified, he said, "A Sirfessor is a knight of knowledge among benighted bipeds peddling pestiferous piffle!"

The rest of his pseudonym had accrued to him because he had actually spent a couple of years in the Klondike, and he had quite a number of photographs of himself in that unlikely milieu to prove it. At any rate, he was always toting around a badly torn briefcase, and he also had scads of untidy manuscripts leaking from all of his overcoat pockets. He was a short, fattish, high-complexioned man with a snuff-stained, whitish mustache, and from under his shaggy eyebrows his pale-blue eyes looked in constant amusement at a world he was forever weighing in the balance. His scales were loaded by his not inconsiderable learning coupled to a rancorless disenchantment which was particularly appealing to an adolescent like myself. He talked very softly, like an elderly college professor who no longer bothers to be heard above the racket of his foolish, inattentive students, but if he happened to find an unusually interested listener, as *I* surely was, he spoke with great precision, as if it were all being taken down in shorthand. That's how it happens that after all this time I can still remember, almost verbatim, about half a dozen of his most frequently reiterated harangues. The one on Human Behavior went something like this:

"You can take my word for it that women would never have bothered to invent sexual morality. That was a real *man*-made piece of contrivance. Later on, when sexual faithfulness, or its equivalent, guaranteed lifelong support for them, the women naturally enough fell in with the idea. Why not? Actually all their natural instincts were against it. I really don't know why I said *sexual* morality, since I believe that the whole notion of morals represents a peculiarly male hunk of intellectual strategy. It's been the law of the world since its very beginning that mobs of the totally inept have consistently devised rules to keep the unusually able somehow in check.

"We were all nomads when we first started until, finally, women began to collect the larger grass seeds and the edible cereals and decided to settle down to get food out of the earth. They were good and sick of traveling anyway; that's no way to raise children, don't you see? Then the men, whom they were supporting by agriculture, went to their secret clubhouse each morning—it was a place particularly tabu for females—and started to boast to one another about the bumper crops they were raising down in the valley. I'm convinced that, later on, when one of these idle loudmouths had, through his wife's unremitting labor, managed to amass a considerable property, he got up one fine day and invented for himself the altogether new concept of 'Honesty.' I'm sure that Honesty was conceived by someone who *owned* something. To a nonpropertied person, such an idea is sheer academic balderdash. Besides, man just loves to blow himself inside of such soap bubbles. Since he can't give birth to a baby, he is constantly fecundating his own imagination with all sorts of chimerical pregnancies. The results are mostly just a lot of deaf and blind hobbyhorses. Of course, in certain exceptional cases a Sirfessor might come through with something that actually has wings; but that happens so rarely and affects such a small number of people that it doesn't really merit more than just a minute asterisk. By and large, man generally comes up with some kind of law or new moral concept to protect the worldly possessions of the thoroughly incompetent. If anybody owns more property than he can conveniently take care of by himself, even if his whole damned family comes around to help him, then it's high time to step in with some kind of a useful moral. Don't touch this! Because, if you do, an unseen power is sure to see you and will make a note of it. At first, they only enslaved women with their blasted tabus, and then they proceeded to lay down the law for the more nimble-witted and the muscularly powerful who were also shamefully poor. As you can see, they succeeded in subduing everybody with nothing but a handful of moral maxims. More powerful than any sledgehammer, morals are—and, what's more, they work all around the clock every day of your life. Oh, yes, man is an ingenious little manipulator, ain't he, though? He wanted his own true blood to inherit all of his ill-gotten property; that's why he had to make sure that no interlopers ever crept into the family hayloft. This bill of schmaltz went over so well—it had so much style, don't you see—that all of the vain troglodytes who owned nothing but the dirt on their skins insisted that strict virtue be maintained by their womenfolk, lest their fungoid toenails and their tartar-stained incisors be inherited by some unlicensed wood colts. Yes, my boy, there's nothing like knowing that, after you're gone, your own flesh and blood is going to make a great big bonfire out of your lifelong swindlings and contrivings. It makes you rest quieter in your grave to know that all you managed to amass through a lifetime of unremitting cruelty, perjury, and oppression your own true heir is going to piss away in one big splash before sunup. I tell you it's peace on earth, boy—that's what it is; it's peace on earth with compound interest!"

As you can see, the Sirfessor Klondike was quite a cat. I liked so much to listen to him that every once in a while I used to buy him a drink, although I've always hated saloons and hated every single damned thing that used to go on inside of them. I know they are called The Poor Man's Clubs; well, I suppose I must have been much too poor and was never really sufficiently lonesome to ever put up with such stuff. But, what the hell, for the sake of a little good talk I managed to blind myself to these dismal surroundings and, what's more, I even lived long enough to tell about it.

CHAPTER EIGHT

A POLISH WRITER NAMED Jerzy Peterkiewitz has written: "I would go so far as to call the artist's childhood his only authentic present; all other stages of time experienced by him will merely indicate the depth of perspective between two static points—childhood and death."

Let me say this: now, when I have decided to call a halt to my rambling reminiscences, I am drawn with an almost irresistible force toward thinking mostly about my very earliest beginnings in Austria. It is as if certain important aspects of my existence had received their axiomatic authority back at the start of this century and the rest of my life consisted of nothing more than a constant re-verification of the essential psychic geometry which defined the emotional facets of my childhood.

I will tell you just a little more about those dear young days in Vienna, where I used to plant myself out on the Johannesfeld

(St. John's Field) on early summer afternoons and watch my kite as it vacillated erratically across the freshly laundered skies.

Now that I come to think about it, it comes back to me that I used to weep quite frequently when I was a child. I recall that sometimes I buried my face in the jasmine bushes that grew behind our house and, as I drank in their incredible fragrance, I would suddenly burst into tears because of the incommunicable ecstasy that flooded my childish being.

You know that the Danube is a very wide river, as wide as the Mississippi in some places, and occasionally, toward dusk, as I sat on the moss-grown banks up near Deutsch-Altenburg, I recall that I was, from time to time, so completely suffused by the mingled aroma of rotting timber, decaying leaves and night-blooming creepers that I could hardly keep myself from bawling out loud with the sheer enchantment of it all. I would look out between the silhouetted willow branches and see white sails, like Japanese ghosts, floating across the gray-green stillness of the un-ruffled stream, and, sometimes, I became literally breathless with the almost intolerable beauty of the visible world all around me.

Since I was frequently ill, there were many occasions when I would lie in convalescent luxury in a hammock out in our garden, and in the springtime it once happened that the flowering cherry trees, shaken by a sudden gust of wind, showered their bridal whiteness down upon me. In a state bordering close to the hallucinal, I then experienced the tiptoeing of the blossoms across my uplifted face before they slowly, ever so slowly, tumbled on down toward the long fingers of the trembling grass.

I will also speak about the occasion my father took me to the museum of art for the first time, and what sort of incoherent, but nevertheless compelling, resolve was born in my heart on that blessed afternoon and how this most momentous visit eventually came to set the characteristic tone for all the rest of my days.

Since the date of that event became highly significant to me, I can tell you exactly when it happened. It was April 6, 1907, when I stepped through those exalted portals and saw what I had secretly been yearning for in a great many clairvoyant dreams—

70

namely, the still and exquisite order which prevailed only in the world of art.

As we wandered slowly through those high, holy rooms I did not really try to achieve full understanding of any of those fabulously painted pictures, or those superb statues poised in gestures of everlasting finality all about us. I was deeply content to be merely surrounded by those smoothly articulated works of man, and despite the churning ambivalence of my childish mind I was, deep down, somehow blindly and desperately resolved to become part of this altogether magical sphere.

You who are grown up and, perhaps, still enter a museum like a stranger trespassing upon an aloof and even frigid company will have difficulty in understanding the almost mystical rapture with which I gazed at all those assembled masterpieces as their shapes and colors first broke upon the horizon of my awareness.

I was determined to study, to work or, if the occasion should arise, to perpetrate any sort of conceivable mayhem only to gain entrance to these cherished precincts; I was willing and ready to become a hounded stowaway on those esoteric premises, and you may believe me that neither ambition nor glory were even distantly contributive factors to my resolve. At any rate, not at that early age.

I would paint, I would sculpt, and my life would be utterly dedicated to the pursuit of the sort of mirages which lived in the minds of certain choice and cherished men who were called "Artists."

I went back to that museum endless numbers of times, and, since I did possess some undeniable precocity in matters of draftsmanship, this, coupled with my tenacity and my luck, eventually landed me in an art school. I was only eight years old then, but fortunately the Secessionist Group in Vienna had decided to accept three gifted children for scholarships each year—and that's how I happened to make it.

It is strange how my preoccupation with art was duly misunderstood by most of the other children that I came to know at that time. One particularly bright, close friend of mine called

Nandor Szábo invited me to spend a few weeks with him at his family's estate near Budapest. It was during our summer vacations, of course, and after a good deal of backward and forward correspondence among our elders I was finally allowed to make the trip. Now then, my friend Nandor's birthday came on July 31, and we were given twenty guilders by his father—a lot of money in those days—to spend in any way that we wished. Naturally, we decided to go to the nearby capital. I'm telling you all this just to show you what a dear boy my friend was and yet how completely he managed to misunderstand me.

When Nandor and I hit Budapest it was nearly noon, so the two of us went to a fine terrace restaurant for our luncheons. My friend's family had properly apprised the management of our coming, and our unchaperoned repast caused only mildly amused head-wagglings. The minute we had finished our meal, Nandor said: "And now, let us go and visit the museum. I know that that will be a real treat for you."

I was deeply touched by his courtesy; he was only a year older than I, but, in certain worldly matters, he already possessed a self-assured maturity which was still largely lacking in my own character. The way he paid the bill and tipped the waiters, not forgetting the busboy, had a quiet authority which impressed me very much.

At any rate, the doorman of the restaurant got us a carriage and off we went to the museum. When we arrived there, I had a terrible shock; it turned out to be the Museum of Natural History. Well, I didn't make a peep. *Noblesse oblige.* I went dutifully from case to case in that huge building, and allowed my friend to believe that I was inordinately devoted to staring at ossified trees and that I was also passionately concerned about the flora and fauna of the Ituri forest. After all, it was *his* special holiday and he had gladly given up a good part of it for my pleasure, so the least I could do was to pretend that I was enjoying it all immoderately.

Many years later, when both of us were already married, Nandor himself recalled that childhood birthday of his. "I took you to the wrong museum, didn't I?" he said. "I must say, you were very nice about it. You can't really blame me. I did it only to please you; actually, any museum was a bore to me in those days. I was just dying to get out to the carrousels and the shooting galleries at the Liget, and it was only after you went to art school a few months afterward that it occurred to me that I had taken you to the wrong place."

"Well, we did go to the Liget finally, didn't we?" I said. "We not only went, but we ate so much spun candy and had so many frankfurters and such endless glasses of cider to go with it all that both of us became deathly sick before the day was over."

"Yes," said Nandor. "We had to stay in bed the following day just to recuperate, and that's also when you told me the beautiful story of Heinrich Heine's early love affair with the daughter of a hangman. Remember?"

It was shortly after my return from Hungary that I discovered the close relationship which exists between all the arts. When I was taken to the theater, or to the opera, or to a concert, I was flooded with the certainty that the composers, the actors, and the singers were, each of them, in their unique, divergent ways trying to realize some special aspects of the world which haunted the minds of all artists, no matter where or how they might be occupying themselves.

It was a big discovery.

Later, after many years in New York, I returned to Austria and the museum where my imagination had been so happily fecundated, and these homecomings were almost in the nature of pilgrimages which a grateful initiate renders at the shrine of his first illumination. Unfortunately, nothing else in Austria was up to my memory of it. The place and the people had undergone terrible disasters, and the alterations in every*thing* and in every*one* proved quite fatal to my idyllic relationship with the past.

Indeed, it took several voyages to the Old Country to convince me that it had become a hopelessly alien territory which was destined to be forever lost to my deeper emotions.

You know, I am sort of vaguely embarrassed that I have managed to write more or less coherently about all these minutely significant matters. I have the feeling that a man ought to mislay his proper voice and lose every grace of utterance when he comes so close to the true origins of his identity.

At any rate, I used to cross the ocean every two or three years just to take another gander at the grayish-brown Danube and to see if anything in the old burg had possibly changed for the better. I still had a few relatives left in Vienna, of course, and most of the sane ones among them were profoundly puzzled by my strong but obviously misdirected homing instincts.

On one of my earlier visits to Austria, my cousin Hugo tried to help find a suitable apartment for me. I needed a pretty good-sized place since I had brought my wife and children along, too, and so, early one Saturday afternoon, my cousin and I set out together to case a few places that were located in a not too unreasonably decayed neighborhood. In those days, around 1928, this wasn't really as easy as it sounds.

Austria seemed to have single-handedly lost the First World War, and if a window was broken anywhere in Vienna it was sure to stay broken forever afterward. There was no merchandise in most of the stores, and the majority of the people I met were unashamedly on the dole.

Well, the first place we looked at was located in a dilapidated building in a once rather fashionable neighborhood. We had been told by the agent who had furnished us this address that the current occupant was a retired actress who was eager to sublet, particularly to foreigners. I could easily pass for a foreigner as long as I didn't talk too much. If I kept on jabbering for more than a minute, my old Austrian accent was sure to break through and that would end my interesting extraterritorial status. Of course, the reason this dame and everybody else wanted to deal only with foreigners was because it was justly assumed that the local nationals were all busted.

We knocked on the designated apartment door for fully five minutes before the tenant *in situ* finally opened. I decided that she couldn't possibly have been delayed by any aspect of her wardrobe, since she hardly had anything on. She wore a large dirty sweater over her nightgown, and this sweater, which was of a mottled gray and unbelievably hairy, was held together by an enormous safety pin. The nightgown, which peeped out underneath, was appropriately raveled on the bottom, and as my prospective landlady wiped her mouth with the back of her hand the reason for her delay in answering the door became instantly clear; she had taken a swig of something just to strengthen herself for this interview, I suppose, and whatever the hell she had been imbibing was now pretty effectively flowing out of every one of her facial apertures. Her pale, washed-out eyes were filled with alcoholic tears, and a dangerously corpulent drop was teetering precariously on the very tip of her fleshy nose. Although she was short and dumpy, she was still a lively load of superannuated coquettishness, and after I'd handed her a couple of helpful Kleenexes she raised some dirty, beringed fingers to her poor, scraggly hair and said: "Those terrible beauty-parlor people are so busy I couldn't get an appointment until this evening." After she'd used up my paper tissues she gave a coy wiggle with that undulating rump of hers and said: "You've probably noticed I'm suffering terribly from hay fever. Would you be kind enough to oblige me with a few more of those little napkins?"

Although I'd never heard of such acute cases of hay fever happening toward the end of December, I handed over the rest of my tissues and said, "Do you think we could look at the apartment now? You see, I have three other appointments this afternoon, and so I'm really somewhat in a hurry."

"Ah, yes, rush, rush, rush," she said, ogling the both of us commiseratively. "That is the modern tempo. Well, I'm sorry to say I'm completely out of step with all this madness. I have to have time to arrange my mind for every new event of the day. You see, I believe in calm composure."

"You *do* want to rent this apartment, don't you?" I said. "Because if you don't—"

"Of course, by all means!" She took me affectionately by the arm and proceeded to lead us through what turned out to be an enormous series of desperately ill furnished caves. There was no heat of any kind, and despite my heavy, wool-lined overcoat I had a tough time to keep my teeth from chattering. This probably explained why this ex-diva, or whatever the hell she was, had to keep hitting the bottle pretty consistently.

It turned out that our hostess was called Mme. Angelika Lichinski, and she confessed to us, with her hand on her greatly enlarged heart, that once her beauty had been known to jeopardize the safety of empires. This statement seemed perfectly feasible to me, since I knew that *some* European empires had populations that, numerically at least, could easily have been ensconced in a couple of city blocks back in New York. In any event, even if Mme. Lichinski had *never* endangered the emotional equilibrium of certain exalted royal personages, she certainly *talked* and *behaved* as if she *had*, and that was surely enough for Hugo and me. As she rattled on, she held one loose flap of her nightgown daintily raised, as if she expected at any moment to throw a profound curtsy to Prinz Windischgraetz-Hohenlohe-Schillingsfuerst. Her poor flabby face, completely ravaged from years of bad makeup and bad liquor, was puckered into nodules of quivering innuendos, and her nose looked as if a discouraged sculptor had slapped it on anyhow just before he finally threw the whole misshapen structure into a garbage pail.

Mme. Lichinski ushered us slowly around her subarctic grotto, and I can assure you that no chatelaine who had just returned from a successful expedition with her favorite falcons and was showing some visiting royalty to their carefully prepared sleeping quarters could have done it with more circumstantial *éclat* than she did. When you consider that she had four pretty important teeth missing and that her greenish-gray hair looked like the foliage of a feather duster that had been subjected to shock treatments, you will realize how inevitable it was that I should, finally, have become deeply moved by her extraordinary performance. The old girl was pure style.

Also, I can tell you that that apartment of hers was truly the most suitable setting for the particularly heartbreaking disaster she represented. It was all just an ultimately baroque junk shop. There was absolutely no end of teetering three-legged end tables, and not a single chair among the eighteen that I counted matched any other chair or any other piece of furniture in that whole musty mausoleum of hers. There was such a plethora of exploding couches around this dump that some of her horsehair derelicts had to be moved out of the way before you were able to pass from one room to another. When I pointed this out to her, she said, "Those sofas aren't heavy at all. I'm much older than either of you, and I move them all the time." She gave me a look of maternal commiseration. "After all, we here in Vienna are still a little old-fashioned; we still do *some* things with our hands. We don't just press a lot of buttons and—presto!—everything moves by itself."

In the living room, in the place of honor between two theatrically draped windows, there hung an enormous oil portrait of someone who looked like Queen Elizabeth, the ex-empress of the Austria of my childhood. On the lower part of the huge gold-and-dirt-encrusted frame there had been nailed a supersized, dried-out laurel wreath, and in the middle of all this mummified vegetation someone had suspended a large, fly-specked card which said, "Mme. Angelika Lichinski in her role as 'The Girl from New Orleans.'"

"This painting," she said, "won three first prizes at St. Poelten and was bought and presented to me by Count Ludwig Rauchstadt von Ehrenhofer."

"Who painted it?" I asked.

"It is by Nepomuk Luftherz the Younger," she said. "It is considered his best period."

I couldn't help thinking that it was probably everybody's best period but, obviously, things had been going downhill pretty fast ever since.

"Pardon me, Mr. King," said Mme. Lichinski, "but are you by any chance Chinese?"

"No, I'm sorry," I said, "but I'm really just an American."

"Ah, well," she said, "I suppose we can't have everything."

77

"Why?" I asked. "Are you particularly partial to the Chinese?"

"*Partial?* I *adore* them!" She rolled her swollen eyes so far up into her head I was afraid she'd never be able to get those poor bloodshot marbles back down again. "I had two Chinese gentlemen living here once, and I don't recall when in my life I've been as happy as during that time. You see, they hardly ever went out. They smoked a great deal—pipes mostly—but I can only tell you that the smell of that smoke simply entranced me. I prefer the Chinese to all other people in the world. By the way, did you say you were an American?"

"Yes," I said. "I was actually born here in Vienna, but I've been living in America for the past eleven years."

"Ah, well, then," she said; "yes, it is easy to see that this is really an *ideal* apartment for you. It will remind you of your youth. They don't have things like this in America." She made a sweeping gesture toward the broken-down crocks all around her. "Yes," she continued, "these things are the accumulation of a lifetime. They have been *lived* with and were not just ordered out of a catalogue, by mail." She gave an affectionate pat to a ruptured armchair that instantly launched a cloud of dust in my direction. "These things," she went on, "are constantly under my personal care. You see, *I go with the apartment!*"

"What do you mean, *you go with the apartment?*" I said.

"Just *that*. I continue to live here, too. I have a little corner of my own here, my little jewel box, in which I live and which is not for rent, *not for all the gold mines in the world!*" She suddenly puckered her face into twitching lumps of belligerent candle grease and looked sternly about the room as if some foolish, headstrong American millionaire had just offered her half his fortune to vacate her jewel box.

"In that case," I said, "I'm afraid I won't be able to take the apartment. You see, I have two small children, and they are sure to annoy you."

"Children!!!" she screamed. "I *adore* children!!!"

"They are not Chinese children," I said. "They are Americans, and I'm afraid they are pretty noisy sometimes."

78

"I will look after them as if they were my own. Princess Mantziwill's two little dwarf terriers won't stay with anyone except me. All children and animals trust me on sight!" She became so agitated that she suddenly started to belch hysterically. "I'll just step out into the kitchen for a moment and get a sip of water," she said. "Don't move! I'll be right back!"

She ran out of the room and, without another word, Hugo and I fled from the apartment and made it to the street before she even suspected that we were gone.

I've told you about this particular episode so exhaustively because within the following weeks it proved to be the event which jelled the synthesis for my altogether new and true conception of Austria. Mme. Angelika Lichinski was the very epitome of what the Vienna of my childhood had become during the decade that I had been away. She sat amid the wreckage of a past that had had little merit even during the best of times and she kept on crooning and mooning about all of her scattered glories, which I knew had been mostly shoddy and tinsel at the very start.

What had made Austria great had been its geniuses, of course, and these geniuses were, in many instances, not Austrians at all; and even if they really happened to be the genuine, native articles, their chances for starving to death in that great, art-loving kingdom were surely excellent.

Mozart and Schubert died neglected and in literal poverty, while most of the distinguished writers of the country were either Czechs or Jews, whom the *nice* Austrians patronized and the *ugly* Austrians ostracized and whom *all* the Austrians eventually murdered off, just as soon as they finally got around to launching a truly native product: Nazism.

I think it is a great error to credit a country for its artistic talents. After all, Pushkin, Dostoevski, Tolstoi, Turgenev, Chekhov, and dozens of other, lesser-known Russian authors functioned and created their masterpieces in the darkest years of the Czarist empire.

Statesmen, I grant you, can emerge out of the flesh and fiber of a national consciousness.

79

Washington, Hamilton, Jefferson, the Adamses, Franklin, and Lincoln were no mere geographic accidents. But writers, painters, and composers may, or may not, happen anywhere. In fact, it frequently occurs that the very land of their birth proves the least hospitable or sympathetic ground for their labors. The greatest Irish playwrights and novelists of my lifetime had to find their real recognition in other lands. I know that Ireland was busy with its fight for freedom, but so were the Russian intellectuals. Of course, the environmental factors are bound to get into the artist's work, and this is where confusion becomes rife. The peculiarly French character of Molière and the unmistakably American texture of Mark Twain are the natural result of their perceptions, which certainly took place in a specific place at a very specific time. But I maintain that the *talent*—the mysterious *gift* which made them into unique individuals—is not analyzable on the basis of national origins and so cannot be justly credited to the altogether chanceful circumstances of where their births happened to take place. We know that some climates are more favorable for the flourishing of certain legumes, but no one has yet doped out or established the best geographic location for the emergence of artistic genius. The present-day Russians would just love to do that if they could. They're obviously going about it in the wrong way. We are also going about it in the wrong way. It certainly doesn't help us to have a lot of creative writers' congresses popping up all over the place. As far as I can see, that only breeds a great deal of pretentious amateurishness.

Art is the most willful of all the will-o'-the-wisps in the whole world, and where it will decide to flicker next—*nobody* knows.

And as for old Austria, I'm aware that things have changed a lot for the better since I last saw Mme. Lichinski. I've had reports of it and I've seen movies about it, too. I've watched the Austrian citizenry diving under cataracts of whipped cream and doing the breaststroke in almost shoreless lakes of buttered chocolate sauce. *That* is really their true national culture: pastry!

Still, I'm glad things have improved for them and that *tourisme* is flourishing.

Let Them All Eat Cake!

CHAPTER NINE

——————————————

I'M OFF AGAIN on what is usually called a summer vacation. Actually, in my case, this is a complete misnomer, since I
must employ the warmer season especially to reacquaint myself
with the more general run of mankind. Most other times of the
year I meet only artists, actors, producers, and writers of all sorts
and, after a while, I get the feeling that I'm losing touch with
normal, everyday humanity. To rectify this, we try to find some
likely, pleasant spot out in the country and, for about ten weeks,
we attempt to establish a few basic contacts with people who are
not worried about impending publication dates, do not have their
minds full of copyright violations, and are not troubled that the
critics may not take too kindly to their new production of *Romeo
and Juliet*, in which the chief protagonists are, respectively, a
notorious pansy and a flagrant lesbian.

Yes, it is definitely a great relief to get away from all that and
to see a few real trees, without cement trusses, and to hear the

voices of honest-to-God crickets instead of plastic ones, for a change. I need all this for my work, too, because without these seasonal immersions into the basic verities of existence, one's point of view tends to be stultified, tends to become almost incestuously involved with just a small group of reiterative art professionals who only too frequently seem to be quite bereft of a wholesome third dimension.

So, I'm again sitting here in the wilds of New England, and the thickly foliaged branches of the native elms and birches are see-sawing delightfully up and down before my window. My wife is out in the back of the house doing a spell of concentrated bird watching, while my nearest neighbors seem, as usual, to be listening to the seductive calls of their radios.

"If mild bladder irritation is making you restless," says a confidentially alarming voice, "if it is making your days and your nights a source of constant uneasiness, then *Nexus* is your answer. Buy the large economy size and spare your irritated bladder the discomfort that brings nausea, insecurity, and a bad complexion."

Well, you can't really escape the benefits of civilization altogether no matter where the hell you go nowadays. It doesn't bother me too much, since there are large compensations in meeting some of the local residents and hearing about problems which are, in many ways, a great deal less egotistically anchored than the ones that are dished up to me, most of the year, by a lot of self-immersed showfolk down in the heart of New York City.

A couple of weeks ago, Margie and I were invited to a little party not too far away from here, and, since this was really our first big opportunity to meet the bucolic gentry en masse, we were naturally quite keyed up about it and hoped that we'd succeed in making a reasonably decent impression on everybody.

This party was being held on somebody's lawn, of course, somebody who obviously made a very good living on Wall Street or maybe out in Hollywood, since most of the guests, although total strangers to me, had that special look of well-heeled outdoorsiness that you simply don't acquire by just hanging out in New England all the year round. No, these boys and girls had definitely achieved their tanned hides in Palm Beach, in Taormina or in Southern California somewhere, because our local sun just isn't consistent enough to give you that special old-cowhide-suitcase kind of appearance.

Margie, who planned to take a swim in the staggeringly outsize pool which graced these premises, went off to put on her bathing suit, while I, who possess no minor vices—that is to say, I don't drink—plunked myself quietly down on one of those unreliable aluminum beach chairs and made an elaborate pretense of having a wonderful time nestling up against the meticulously depilated bosom of nature.

Since there were about a dozen or so such seating and reclining devices stacked alongside of me, it wasn't very long before a few of the carefully coiffed, sun-cured effigies came along to join me.

I was particularly fortunate because one of the most striking-looking women in the place chose to put her chair right beside mine and, in less than two minutes, we were up to our eyebrows in animated conversation. I should have said "disheveled" eyebrows, because when I stated that this female was striking-looking, I did not mean that she was beautiful or that, conceivably, she ever *had* been. She was more like one of those wind-and-weather-worn ship's effigies that you can see for sale in some of the more imaginative antique shops on upper Third Avenue. I couldn't quite make up my mind how old this sea-maiden might really be, but I was certain that she played a deadly game of croquet and I was equally sure that she would make a highly exigent and bitterly reproachful bridge partner. She was tall and bony, and I was convinced that the confused follicles on her multicolored head could no longer remember what the original tint of her hair could possibly have been. Her eyes were blue and penetrating and her nose would have been sufficiently authoritative for Lord Nelson, even at the battle of Trafalgar. I forgot to mention that she had a voice like an extinct volcano, and she used it to such good purpose on the white-coated catering staff that was busying itself all around us that her glass was never empty for more than thirty seconds during the entire hour and a half that she had decided to keep me in her thrall.

At first she talked to me chiefly about the worthlessness of gardeners and groundkeepers, and before I could establish where and how all these difficulties happened to poison her life, a rather swollen looking, glandular-type girl approached her and proceeded to whisper some personal problems into her ear.

My vis-à-vis, whose name, by the way, was Clarice Holstack (Miss? Mrs.?), listened attentively to this overstuffed cornucopia and finally said, "Don't worry, Ginny; I'll have that saddle taken care of first thing Monday morning."

After the saddle worrier had gone off, the Holstack woman turned to me and said, "That's one of the most heartbreaking stories I've ever had anything to do with. It is really difficult to believe what sort of things go on right under our very noses."

I tried very hard to look appropriately sympathetic. "Is her saddle in such a very bad shape, then?" I asked tentatively. I didn't really care one way or another. I just wanted to keep things rolling the way you always do at parties. So I continued: "Is the young lady related to you, by any chance?"

"Oh, no," she said. "As a matter of fact, this poor child comes from a perfectly dreadful home. You can't possible imagine what goes on among these irresponsible people. Her father and mother don't just throw things at each other—they *shoot* at each other *through windows!* Would you ever *believe* that such things are *possible?*"

"Well," I said, "if the provocation is strong enough, who knows what all is liable to happen?"

"But that's not the worst of it," she said. "About a week ago they had another brawl, and when Ginny—that is the child's name —when Ginny tried to quiet them down, they simply threw her out of the house; threw her out at eight o'clock in the evening with just the clothes she had on her back—and her horse, of course."

"They threw her out with her *horse?*" I said.

"Yes, they just wanted to get rid of her and have no further responsibilities. A horse takes a lot of bother, you know, and those two selfish monsters certainly wanted no part of *that*."

For a moment I couldn't help wondering about a lot of other people who had been thrown out of homes, and I had to confess to myself that I had never before in all of my life heard of anyone's being chucked out in company with a horse. No matter how you considered it, it was certainly a complication.

"So what happened?" I asked.

"What happened? She came to me, of course. I live right down the road from them, and I sometimes used to go riding with her; so, when she didn't know where to turn at that late hour, she just came up and knocked on my door. Fortunately, I had no guests, so I had plenty of room for both of them; so, after she'd cried her poor heart out and seen her horse properly taken care of, I lent her a nightgown, gave her a couple of sleeping pills and put her into my downstairs bedroom."

"And then?"

"Well, you see, the whole business was much more tragic than you can ever realize. The poor dear had her heart set on riding in the *Freewater Cross Country Club Joust*, which was scheduled for the following Sunday, and she'd been preparing herself for this event for almost five weeks. And then, those unspeakable parents of hers just flung her out in the middle of the night without a proper riding habit—without even a measly pair of jodhpurs to cover her shanks—and the whole project suddenly went right up the flue. No outfit—no ride; that's all."

"You've got me right on the edge of this chair," I said. Actually, it was more like having one leg caught in an oversized aluminum mousetrap, but the Holstack woman was so touched by my evident interest that she went right on.

"Luckily, I always have some spare clothes around the house," she said. "Sometimes people come unprepared and occasionally we have accidents and people's clothes get torn—so I quickly got hold of a little seamstress from over Fillbank way and within about two days everything was properly taken care of. That is, everything but her *hat*. Nothing I owned would fit her. I was in absolute despair."

As my neighbor paused for a moment to have her drink replenished I quickly looked over at Ginny, who, without her horse, made a rather forlorn figure. I observed her kicking some random stones into the swimming pool, and, as I stared at her, I was not at all surprised that she'd had difficulties in finding a hat. Her head, now that I was examining it with more care, was shaped like a lopsided cantaloupe, or perhaps a small Zeppelin that was quickly losing air.

"And did she finally ride *without* a hat?" I asked, turning back to my refueled informant.

"*Of course not.*" The mere idea of such a flagrant breach of horse protocol made her positively snort. "That was out of the question. But one of my upstairs maids, Amelia, has a boyfriend who works in the firehouse, and his head is shaped a good deal like Ginny's."

"Now *that* was lucky," I said. I really couldn't imagine that it could possibly be lucky for anybody to have such a crazy-looking noggin, but, frankly, I was so carried away by the story that I hardly noticed *what* I was saying.

"It was a plain black derby hat and needed a lot of alterations, but, even so, by Saturday afternoon I knew we had our problem licked."

"And Ginny *rode*," I said.

"She *rode* and she *won!* Can you *imagine* it? Her dreadful parents were there, too, of course, and when it was all over and the toasts had been given and the cup had been presented—these two cringing vandals came over to congratulate her."

"It must have been quite a scene," I said. "I'm sorry I missed it."

"And well you *may* be. I can't tell you how *pleased* I was. That wretched mother of hers put her arm around her and said, 'Ginny, darling, come on home; we've been ever so lonesome without you.' She's their only child, you see. And then that nasty old cocklebur, that father of hers, chimed in, too. 'Ginny, old girl,' he said, 'I'll help you walk the champion, if you like; what do you say?' "

"And what did Ginny do?" I said.

"Oh, you would have been proud of her. She just looked at them quietly for about half a minute and then she said, 'No, thanks. Gustaf and I'—Gustaf is the name of the horse—'Gustaf and I will make out quite all right from now on.' "

"So, what did the parents do *then?*"

"Oh, they just looked foolish, of course, and then the mother said, 'Well, we've been turned down for a horse.' And the father said, 'Yes, and for a stinking old *gelding,* too. Well, that's your damned daughter for you.' "

"What a lovely story," I said.

"Yes, lovely, isn't it? I just wish she hadn't been wearing that hideous derby when she told her people to get lost. Unfortunately, she just couldn't pry the thing loose. As a matter of fact, we finally went over to the blacksmith shop at the Grosvenor Stables and had to have it pried off piecemeal. In the end, with just the leather band around her head, she looked just like Joan of Arc—only more American, of course."

"Of course," I said. "The most congenial saints generally do."

CHAPTER TEN

IT MUST BE well over forty years ago that I first started to work on the New York *World* and used to take my midday meals in a little eating place, near Nassau Street, called Carrie's Hot Foods. The reason I favored this particular dump was that they let me eat at a two-seater table (generally reserved just for the help) right near the pay telephone, so that people could reach me even during my lunch hour. I had a very active social life during those days and I was constantly afraid I might be missing something. I usually had that table to myself, but one day an agreeable-looking middle-aged man (everybody over thirty was middle-aged in those days) sat down with me and started to study the bill of fare.

"What would *you* recommend, Mr. King?" he said, smiling puckishly over the top of the fly-specked menu.

"Well, I nearly always have soup and maybe a salad of some kind," I said.

"That sounds like an excellent suggestion," he said. "By the way, my name is Charley Wood, and I heard about you from Bob Ament up at the *World*."

We shook hands, and I must say I took an instant shine to this pleasant noonday intruder.

Later, after we'd finished our meal, we went for a stroll over to City Hall park and, as I sat there beside him on a bench, the title of this present volume came to my ears for the first time.

"Do you believe that there *is* a life after birth?" Charley Wood said, blinking speculatively up at the top of the Woolworth tower.

It was a subject rather close to my heart at that moment. I had never phrased it as succinctly, but some weeks before I had done a series of cartoons for a magazine called *Good Morning*, owned by my friend Art Young, and I had labeled my little opus "The Half Dead." In my drawings I had delineated a series of characters that I had seen around New York—Bowery bums, beggars of all sorts, millionaires enshrined in their Fifth Avenue club windows, and an extremely well-dressed young man who was yawning with all his power as a pretty girl, sitting close beside him, was eyeing him rather seductively.

"I saw your cartoons in *Good Morning*," Charley Wood went on, "and I thought they'd been done by a much older man."

"Well," I said, "I suppose some of us catch on to the idea much earlier than others."

"That's true. I remembered your name, and when I saw Bob Ament yesterday he told me where I'd probably find you eating lunch."

"Just a minute," I said. "Aren't you the Charles W. Wood who wrote a series called 'Beyond and After'?"

"I am," he said. "As a matter of fact, I'm planning to write some more of them and bring them out in a book, maybe."

"Well, I think they're just great," I said. "I've cut them all out and saved them. They *should* be put between covers."

"I'm glad you liked them," he said. "But this other thing—this half deadness that seems to have bothered you; it's been bothering me for quite a while, too. Somebody ought to tackle it and explain it. It might even help a few people just before they're settling down to their own living entombments. I'd even go farther: I'd investigate whether, properly speaking, there aren't a lot of people around whose screams of horror when they first emerged out of their mothers' wombs weren't also the last authentic utterances they were ever destined to make before they passed back into total silence again—the total silence of a meaningless *life*."

Of course, I was greatly stimulated by Charley's far-reaching speculations, and our first meeting was naturally followed by several others, in which he expatiated most wittily and searchingly on the general subject of the human dilemma in the twentieth century. I understand that he eventually put a lot of his shrewd conjecturings down on paper, but since I got married shortly after we met, the all-absorbing problem of an immediately adequate livelihood came to take uppermost place in my consciousness and, for quite a while, I had little enough time for random speculations about the moribund conditions of my fellowmen. That's how it happened that I lost track of Charley and of a lot of other fine people, too; and then, one day, when I read that he had died I couldn't help wondering what ever had become of his manuscript, if there really had been one in the first place.

As far as I am able to discover, nothing publishable on this general theme was ever found among his literary effects. But I am glad to remember this good and gracious comrade, and I am most happy to pay appropriate tribute to his vivacious mind, in which the problem of life after birth was first seriously formulated as a topic for fruitful conjecture.

Incidentally, Peter Schwed, my editor up at Simon and Schuster, has a particularly capable and charming secretary, Nelle Haber, who once used to do quite a bit of typing for Charley Wood. I discovered this only very recently, too. So you can plainly see that there is no end to the benign coincidences which still punctuate my life among the gentiles.

CHAPTER ELEVEN

B<small>EFORE THE SUBJECT</small> of my origins in Austria is forever banished from these pages, I'd like to tell you about two
significant events that took place during my last visit to that
country.

The first of these happenings had to do with my old teacher,
Father Joseph. He had become very dear to me during my student days at the Jesuit school which I finally came to attend (after
my expulsion from the Hanslicht *academia*), and yet, for one reason or another, I had somehow failed to call on him on any of my
previous visits, even while hovering pretty close in his general
vicinity.

When I was back in Europe around 1947, I suddenly felt a
very strong need to see him again. I knew that he was still alive,
because an ex-classmate of mine, Bernard Werner, whom I had
met in Paris, had told me that the old man was still holding occasional unscheduled seminars out at our school.

Father Joseph was the man I always held largely responsible for the fact that I became an avid and discriminating lover of books. When you are young you just have to have a great deal of luck with your teachers, since nothing is easier to frustrate than a child's first, eager curiosity. It is certainly of paramount importance that the trusting, tremulous searchings of a young mind should not become hopelessly mired in a mess of authoritative misinformation and a lot of pedagogical hogwash.

If you're lucky and you get the right break, then your English teacher will be in love with his subject and the whole world of great literature will open up all its treasures to you. If your man (or woman), on the other hand, happens to be just a job-holding timeserver, then, I am afraid, the chances are pretty strong that a deadly load of wretchedly written magazine articles and a slew of idiotically contrived comic books will eventually become the basic foundation for your intellectual diet.

At any rate, I had the fantastic good fortune to land on Father Joseph's doorstep. He was head of the Latin and history departments, but he also taught literature, geography, and art.

I'll give you an idea of the sort of teacher he was: If one of his tuition periods happened to be scheduled just before lunchtime, it frequently occurred that his students would simply ignore the noon-hour bell and quietly pretend that his class was not yet over. I think that this is just about the most stupendous compliment that can possibly accrue to any teacher. Remember, we were only children from seven to nine years old.

Bernard Werner and I were the only non-Catholics among the two hundred and twenty boys who attended school there, and no one on the faculty or on the maintenance staff ever discriminated against us in any way whatever. I daresay the fathers hoped, eventually, to convert us to the true faith, but they certainly never made any overt gestures to steer either of us anywhere near the baptismal font during all of the seven years that I spent with them.

Some of our fellow students were, of course, a great deal less civilized in their attitudes toward Bernie and myself, but, even so, the majority of them often invited us to their homes and, on several occasions, I spent a few weeks of my summer vacation at the villa of a papal count whose son had become a very close friend of mine.

What bound our little group closer together than anything else was our common esteem and affection for Father Joseph. This dear man taught us history as if the events of the past had been inextricably woven into the fabric of our own lives. He had a truly universal concept of the world, and he tried to make us understand the deep interrelatedness of many seemingly far removed events in the long, turbulent story of mankind. He had a wonderful speaking voice, the kindest eyes, and the most durable patience of anyone I ever knew. His joy in catering to our burgeoning perceptions was so evident that if I had not been irrevocably committed to the career of a painter, I would most assuredly have followed his glorious example and become a teacher.

Now then, in the winter of 1947, when I had finally decided to pay him a belated visit, I happened to be mixed up with an American girl, a girl of considerable beauty and even some rather surprising intellectual endowments; and yet, there could be no doubt that this good-looking and often quite witty and well-spoken creature was the victim of a rather acute sterility of the imagination.

Her name was Laura Hartwig. I had met her at an American friend's home in Vienna, and, as she seemed unattached at the moment, I came, eventually, to spend quite a bit of time with her. Some peculiarities of her character proved rather novel to me during those years, but I have since discovered that she was really an American archetype, whose duplicates I have since encountered by the several scores. She had studied, rather desultorily, Buddhism, psychology, art, home economics, and fashion modeling, but a good many of her more concentrated efforts had gone into trying to find some specific merits in several dull and totally unrewarding men. She was most pleasant to look at—tall, auburn-haired, and very fair-skinned—but her outstanding fascination for me was in her amber-colored, green-flecked eyes. The eyes promised *Everything*, which, in a world that is committed to definite limits, was destined to lead to a hang-up. In due time I discovered that despite her course in home economics she was quite incapable of dishing up any sort of halfway decent meal, but since she was really quite bright about some things—bright to talk to, I mean—and as she was also extremely decorative, she happened to suit my limited emotional needs quite satisfactorily.

You see, at that dismal period of my life I was hopelessly addicted to morphine. Around 1945, some doctors back in the States, who had been treating me for kidney stones, had administered such reckless quantities of this stuff to me that before I even had a chance to realize it I was hooked.

I think it was this deplorable situation, more than anything else, which made me suddenly long to see my old teacher again. Although I had not the slightest intention to tell Father Joseph about the disaster which had engulfed me, I yearned to look into his eyes again and, perhaps, to draw some comfort or even strength from the reassuring aura of his mere presence. I daresay the psychiatrists are probably right when they surmise that the poor bedeviled biped called man would like to crawl back into the womb again whenever his mind becomes too heavily burdened by seemingly unsolvable anxiety syndromes.

I suppose that must be the reason why some people, when unusually serious troubles befall them, go straight to bed and cover themselves up right over their heads as a sort of symbolic withdrawal from the world, which seems ready to collapse around their ears.

Whatever the hell the motivation, I, too, in my overwhelming misery, tried to run back into my childhood, back to the study of my beloved mentor, hoping that by some miracle he would lift the secret incubus from my mind and restore me to my normal self again.

At any rate, on a Friday afternoon in late December I took a taxi and drove out to pay my visit to Father Joseph. If I had been my usual, balanced self, I would, of course, have gone alone, but Laura had been badgering me all morning to take her along, too, so I finally abdicated both reason and good taste and took her. Since she spoke only badly fragmented German, I wondered what she would make of it all. "Oh, the hell with it," I finally decided. At any rate, she had gotten herself up with unusual decorum for this trip; she wore a black wool suit, a dark cloth coat, and a small hat with a veil. As far as I could judge, she was dressed fittingly enough to be received with propriety even at the Vatican.

It was a big mistake, just the same, although it didn't seem that way at the beginning.

First of all, I can't tell you how happy and proud I was when I saw how well the old man remembered me. "When you left for the United States, we were in the seventeenth section of *Herodotus*," he said. "Why should you be surprised that I recall it so clearly? After all, you left in April, and that's where we usually are in *Herodotus*."

"That was thirty-three years ago," I said. I noted that he had lost some of his hearing in the intervening period, but his fine, dark eyes still shone with almost youthful enthusiasm.

"How could I forget you?" he said. "I remember that a few days after you arrived here you came to confession. I daresay I had forgotten that you were not a Catholic, and as I listened to you it seemed to me that I heard you rustling some paper. 'What are you doing?' I asked. 'Are you, by any chance, eating candy?' 'No, Father,' you said. 'It's just a piece of paper on which I have written down my sins. I have trouble making out the writing because it is so dark in here.' 'You've written down your sins on paper?' I said—and then it suddenly occurred to me that you were not supposed to come to confession at all. I realized that, in your childish eagerness to be like all the other children, you had come to confession but you had come prepared with a whole list of written trespasses. It was just like you to do a thing like that. Yes, I sometimes used to watch you in our speech and rhetoric classes, and I used to say to myself, 'Alexander, Alexander, you are a salamander.' "

He was frail, of course, but not really feeble, and I rejoiced to see that his hands did not tremble unduly when he reached for his small desk file. "I have had some correspondence with my old pupils over the years," he said. "Do you recall Herbert Hansmann, by any chance? He was one form ahead of you, I believe, but he was president of the students' council for three succeeding semesters and I thought you might still remember him."

"I do indeed," I said. "He was the *primus* of every class during his whole stay here, wasn't he, Father?"

"Yes," he said. "I've just had another letter from him a few weeks ago. He is a missionary-physician in British East Africa, and his younger brother just left very recently to join him out there." Father Joseph had absentmindedly been fingering his desk file while he talked to me, and I believe he would have read me Herbert Hansmann's letter if I had been alone with him. When I had first introduced Laura, the old man had acknowledged her presence with a smile of infinite sweetness; however, he had not once again looked at her, or even in her direction, during all the rest of my visit.

"It was very kind of you to pay me a call," he said, "and I would like to give you a little keepsake to take back to America with you." He opened the top right-hand drawer of his old-fashioned mahogany desk and took out a very small, beautifully embroidered half-slipper. As he placed this treasure before me, I could feel all the feathers on Laura's neck bristling with intense curiosity. I didn't actually *see* her, because she had very discreetly placed herself a little behind my line of vision, but I didn't *have* to see her to sense the intense concentration of her stare as it tried to encompass the meaning of this peculiar token. Father Joseph held up the slipper before me for a moment and said, "It is lovely, isn't it?"

"Yes," I said, "it is exquisite. Is it *petit point?*"

"Yes," he said. "It was done by some nuns, many years ago, for some great abbot who had come upon a visit from a far land. I have a little note about it somewhere, and if you will give me your address I will have it forwarded to you. At any rate, after passing through many hands, the slippers finally came to me. Unfortunately my feet were never small enough to wear them; also, I think they are really too beautiful for common use. I'm giving you this one in memory of our pleasant days together. I've sent the other one off, with Hansmann's brother, to Africa. You see, I'm clearing up my estate. I will be ninety-four next May, and I think I had better start bestowing my possessions, don't you?"

At this point I could feel Laura's breath on the back of my neck as she said to me, in English, "What is he saying? I don't get all of it. Is he making you a present of those adorable slippers? May I please look at them?"

"There is only *one*," I said, without turning around. Then I got up, stepped around the desk, and warmly embraced my old teacher. I put the slipper quickly into my coat pocket, took Laura by the arm, and convoyed her out of the room.

I was pretty badly shaken, but, by the time we had reached the huge stone pillars near the school entrance, I had achieved sufficient control over my vision to take one long, last look at the weatherworn buildings and at the moss-covered slates upon their ancient roofs.

The taxi had been waiting for us, and the moment we got inside, Laura, naturally, started at once with her pent-up litany of frustrations. "Well, I must say I've certainly seen an altogether unexpected side of you, Friar Alexander."

"I told you not to come along with me," I said. "I told you he's just an old man, and the miracle is that he remembered me at all."

"Oh, it isn't *that*," she said. "It's just the way you *looked* at him and the way you both *acted* about that silly slipper of his. You were like members of a secret organization exchanging symbolical fetishes. He *is* a Jesuit, isn't he?"

"*I'm* not," I said. "Besides, what has *that* got to do with it?"

"Oh, I don't know—the way you understood one another like brothers of the same frat, who know all the passwords and everything."

I was suddenly very tired.

"He gave me a keepsake in memory of the seven happy years I spent in that house. He doesn't expect anybody to *wear* it. He is afraid that he may not live until his next birthday, and so he is getting rid of all his earthly property—don't you understand? Probably everything he owns is lying around in the drawers of his desk. He's sent one slipper off to another pupil of his in Africa, and he gave me this one because he was happy I had cared enough to come back and visit him. The gift is very dear to me because, in a manner of speaking, it is *la pantoufle de mon confesseur*, and if you had read a story under that title and with that general substance in Flaubert or in Balzac, you'd have made a lot of notes in the margins and, eventually, you would probably have gotten class credit for it!"

I had never seen Laura look more startled as she unconsciously backed away from me, and her ever-promising orbs were positively clouded with honest bewilderment.

Of course, I was instantly sorry that I had let her have it in this crude way. After all, I had her pretty well taped by that time and I should have known what to expect from her. I'd been letting out a good deal of my disappointment in myself at her expense, and, secretly, I was probably happy to have had her along for a scapegoat. I had expected I don't know *what* out of this interview with Father Joseph and, now that it was over, I was hung up higher than a tattered kite fluttering helplessly on some wind-tossed telephone wires. I had deliberately dipped back into my past, and with the help of my revered teacher I had roused up all the ghosts of my wonderful childhood. I had been greatly upset by this visit, and I felt helpless and ashamed that my life, which had held so much promise, should have ended so prematurely at the complete mercy of my sordid vice. I longed to throw myself at someone's feet and ask to be purged of my uncleanness; I wanted to achieve some sort of absolution and to resume my place as a responsible member of society once more. But I realized only too clearly that things could not be solved that simply for me. I was a man alone with his curse and I would have to walk step by step toward disaster or salvation with only the hope that my *reason* and my *will* would again learn to take command of my destiny.

I went back to my hotel, took a long, hot bath and thought about many, many things, trying to conjure up some feasible foothold for my possible ascent out of the depths. But after a while my naturally buoyant spirits came to my rescue and I decided, for the time being, just to go on from day to day, taking the goodness and the misery as it came, and to continue hoping that some incalculable twist of fate, some puffball of magical thistle seeds would come my way and carry me off to an enchanted world of peace and safety.

Meanwhile, there was Laura, of course.

She wasn't really a bad sort. Heaven knows she had been amiable enough in relieving me of my boredom and my loneliness, and I had certainly been unduly waspish to her about Father Joseph's slipper. I decided to make it up to her somehow.

Toward evening I went into one of those fancy leather-goods shops with which Vienna abounds, and, handing my precious slipper to one of the clerks, I said to him: "I want you to cut the back of this slipper off altogether and put some silver—*real* silver —rings around the upper part of the cone which will then remain. You see, I want to make a tiny lady's evening bag out of it, with a black silk cord drawn through the rings."

The clerk wasn't astonished in the least. It was precisely the sort of commission that would appeal to the imagination of a Viennese knickknack dispenser. "I understand," he said. "I'll have it ready for you by the middle of the coming week."

The following Wednesday I presented Laura with the new evening bag. She was absolutely enchanted with it. During all of our peculiar communion I had never seen her so rapturously gay.

"Oh, you cunning devils," she said. "I should have known. Nobody in Austria is too old or too holy to think of doing something chivalrous for a lady. So *that's* what the old boy really had in mind all the time. Do you know—I've got a good notion to go back and give the old darling a great big kiss for that."

However, since she didn't get any encouragement from me, she, happily, let the whole matter drop.

Father Joseph did live to see two more birthdays before he finally died. Laura is married, has two children and is now living in California. Her husband writes popularizations of psychoanalytical subjects, and I understand she is of great help to him in his work. All of his products are affectionately dedicated to her, and his latest paperback even features her as a coauthor.

The last time I saw Laura was in New York City about twelve years ago, and she told me that she still owned and frequently carried the evening purse made out of Father Joseph's slipper.

"I'll treasure it always," she said. "You know, at that time, in Vienna, I saw a facet of your character I would never have believed you actually possessed."

"Is that so?" I said. "I don't recall that I was particularly different then."

"Oh, yes, you were! When you talked to that old priest you acted altogether like one of his most devout parishioners. No one would ever have suspected that you were a slick, worldly article without a shred of faith anywhere about you. In fact, I think you were absolutely mealymouthed in the way you sat there and buttered him up."

"I'm sorry, Laura," I said. "I'm sorry that you should have so thoroughly misread my relationship to my old teacher, although, I suppose, that must be a common enough error among psychological vacuum cleaners and professional categorizers. You missed altogether the fact that this old man had, for a great many decades, given all his time and his energy to being useful to the young people who came under his care. He gave them inflexible ethical guidance not only by the things he *said* but by everything that he himself *was*. I lived in that same small world with him for seven of my most fortunate years, and I never saw him self-righteous or impatient with anyone, no matter how trying the occasion. I think I can guess what you mean, though; since you know that I don't subscribe to the religious doctrines which were sacred to him, you assume that our whole relationship was based on pure hypocrisy. Well, you couldn't possibly be more in error. I believe in the physical evolution of man, but I believe just as fervently in his possible *moral* evolution as well. Let me tell you that Father Joseph, and quite a number of his kind, have channeled this moral evolution of the children who were entrusted to them with a selfless devotion and passion that can probably not be matched anywhere on this earth. You make another mistake because you know that more people have been killed for religious causes than for probably any other reasons in the world. You are aware, for instance, that when the Puritans, after fleeing from their religious persecutors, came to America and set up their pulpits in New England, the first thing they did was to inaugurate their own little punitive systems, which resulted in water-dippings, public pillories and large-scale witch-burnings. I know all about that, too. These bloody, tyrannical excesses of *all* organized religions have, of course, always filled me with horror. But what I can't help thinking about is that Stone Age man didn't just naturally grow an automatic code of ethics by leaving it all up to the mere process of evolution. I don't believe anything of the sort. I think that *Somebody, somewhere*, bothered to invent a soul for him, and *that* was surely no small achievement. I think you and I ought to honor and remember gratefully those who patiently and zealously kept this hopeful torch aloft in the darkest times, among the very earliest beginnings of things. How about the unsung, unknown saints who first codified decent neighborly relations among people and who, in return for their services toward the eventual humanization of man, became the targets for the most vicious slander and gossip on the part of their ungrateful fellow creatures? Come, Laura. Don't you think there is a good deal of merit in what I am saying? Admit it; there *is*."

"I think you are an impossible sophist," she said. "In fact, I wouldn't be surprised to find that you'll eventually end up with a shaven pate and a coarse rope around your middle. I really believe you have the basic ingredients for it right now."

I raised my right hand over her frivolously flowered hat and said, "Go in peace, my daughter, and sin no more."

My last story with an Austrian locale took place just a week later, only two days before Christmas. For quite a number of years I used to believe that the Christmas festival—with its decorated evergreens, its lavish displays of baked goods and roast meats, and its abundance of sparkling presents—was a special Austrian invention. I may have been quite right, for all I know, since I'm still certain that only in Japan would it be possible to find an equal plethora of shimmering trinkets and tinseled doodads as my native country abounds in even during the less festive months of the year. The Yule season in Vienna is like being let loose in a Dickens Christmas story on which an altogether unrestrained Lewis Carroll had also been permitted to collaborate. Not only are the shops teeming with a good deal of rational merchandise, but, for this particular occasion, vast numbers of completely unexplainable and totally unusable trifles of all sorts are launched at the public, which, later, in a perhaps somewhat soberer moment, cannot possibly conceive why any of these meaningless fripperies had ever been purchased in the first place.

At any rate, it was December 23 and I was already loaded down with half a dozen elaborately packaged gifts when I suddenly happened to pass in front of a bookshop. Before I knew it, I was inside fingering bindings and riffling pages with the sensuous enjoyment which comes only to the heart of a dyed-in-the-wool bibliophile. Unlike all the other shops in the neighborhood, this store seemed to be almost totally deserted. The owner, an elderly, shrunken figure with a two-days' growth of beard, was warming his bony, arthritic hands over a little round coal stove, while the only other customer in the place was hovering uneasily over a counter laden down with rather large art books. Even if this other customer had not been hung with two cameras and two light meters, I would instantly have spotted him to be an American. You see, when an American, anywhere in Europe, ever goes into a bookshop, he has the lost air of someone who has accidentally strayed into a cemetery around twilight, or even later, and is now halfheartedly passing the time by trying to decipher the inscriptions on the various tombstones.

After a while, my fellow American seemed to have settled on an item that carried more than passing interest for him, and as he lifted up a rather good-sized volume he turned toward the proprietor and said, "How much? Weefeel dis costs?"

"Twenty-five schillings," said the storekeeper.

"Twenty-five schillings?" You could see that the prospective customer was trying to translate these enigmatic figures into sensible dollars and dimes. They counted about seven schillings to the dollar in those days, and, although nobody had asked me, I proceeded to be of help.

"It'll amount to about three and a half dollars altogether," I said.

The American gave me a grateful smile and slowly put down the book.

"Thank you," he said. "I'm looking for something for my daughter, who studies music. This seemed like something that might strike her right, but then, I suppose, you can't really ever tell with girls."

"How old is your daughter?" I asked.

"Going on fifteen, but pretty grown-up for her age. By the way, my name is Stewart Petersen and I'm from Michigan," he said.

After I, in my turn, had introduced myself to Mr. Petersen, it seemed very much as if that good man had completely changed his mind about buying anything that day. He slowly ambled toward the entrance of the store, and as he took the doorknob into his hand he gave just one more vacant look around the large, overloaded shop, smiled at me and, finally, turned his back on us, ready to exit.

At this point the quiet little man, from over the stove, suddenly leaped into frenetic action. "Won't you please wait just a moment!" he said in excellent English. "My name is Oscar Riesel and I am from Vienna." He practically leaped up to the door, and before the man from Michigan knew what was happening to him, he was being led back into the depths of the bookstore again.

Mr. Riesel picked up the volume that Petersen had been considering and held it shoulder-high, like an auctioneer who is waiting for a final bid. "Just take a good look at this book," he said, and, believe me, he wasn't only saying it to the two of us. I had the feeling that he was actually saying it to the world at large, that he was invoking all of mad mankind to pause in its headlong race toward perdition and to consider something very serious for a moment. "This book," he said, "is a specially illustrated edition of the complete score and libretto of the opera *Don Giovanni* with three hundred color prints by the most famous artists in Austria—Klimt, Kokoschka, Marbach, Ruggieri, and sixteen other artists, including Alfred Kubin. It is some of their finest work. Please, please look at it carefully." He held the book out toward the American, who reached for it without much enthusiasm.

"I thought that maybe the music might interest my daughter," said Mr. Petersen. "But I think the binding looks pretty cheap." He turned to me and said, "It does look mighty sleazy, doesn't it? What do *you* think?"

Mr. Riesel didn't wait for me to answer. He took the book out of the American's hand and laid it down on the counter before us. "This book," he said, passing his hand gently over the plain, cardboard cover, "is the complete opera of *Don Giovanni*, one of the greatest masterpieces in the world. This special edition was designed and the plates were all engraved just before the war broke out. Because so many famous artists were connected with this project, it was planned to make this a really deluxe edition. Despite the many critical shortages of necessary raw materials even in the very beginning, you still can see that the paper and the printing are of the very highest order. Of course, later on, when the really bad times came to us and when, during the last months of the war, even the food ran out, this work was completely halted."

Riesel closed his eyes for a brief spell, as if the memory of those bitter times was something more than he cared to go on recalling in the presence of two total strangers who, by the merest accident, had happened to drop into his bookstore just a couple of days before Christmas. Also, I realized that, unlike his neighbors all around him, he was obviously doing no business at all, and I supposed that this was also very probably the reason why a sudden access of seemingly uncontrollable desperation had come into his voice and manner as he had been speaking to us about this publication.

At last he lifted his wrinkled eyelids and said, "There came a time when there was no food at all. If you had a sick child and you had a doctor's certificate, you stood in line a whole night to get half a cup of powdered milk. Sometimes, even then, there was nothing to be had at all. We had reached bottom. So, you see, for quite a while the sheets for this book were lying on the shelf, until the printer made up his mind to bind it somehow, anyhow, just to get it into the shops. But many collectors in Europe prefer to have their books bound to suit their own tastes. As a matter of fact, there are three bookbinders within a short walking distance from here who will bind this book for you, magnificently, for eight or ten schillings. Do you gentlemen know anything about Wolfgang Amadeus Mozart, the man who wrote the opera *Don Giovanni?* Well, let me tell you that he nearly died of hunger. In the end of his life—he was only in his early thirties—his clothes had become so shabby that he had to borrow a coat from a friend whenever he had to go out to interview a prospective employer, who might give him a job as choirmaster or as musical arranger for some music that, maybe, the patron himself had written. Yes, in the end, Mozart looked just like this binding—just as shabby and poor as this poor binding. But, when you *open* this book!"

Riesel opened the book to a beautiful color spread and stared at it for a moment, his face absolutely illumined with pleasure.

"As you can see," he went on, "the *inside* of this *book* is like the *inside* of *Mozart*. All is full of music and full of shining wonder, no matter how shabby the outside might seem to be."

"I'll buy the book, Mr. Riesel," I said, "and I'll also take all those twenty bound volumes of *Jugend* you have on those two lower shelves. You can send them to my hotel tomorrow morning."

"Now, just a minute there!" said Mr. Stewart Petersen from Michigan. "I hadn't really quite made up my mind about this thing yet. I don't think it's quite fair for you to grab it practically out of my hands before I'd actually decided what I was going to do."

"I'll tell you what *I'm* willing to do, Mr. Petersen," I said, "since I have quite *definitely* decided to buy this book. But here's what I'm willing to arrange with you regarding it: you can give it to your little daughter as a present, a Christmas present, from me. At less than fifteen, she may still accept presents from unknown people, as long as her own father acts as the go-between. Tell her it is a gift from an ex-Austrian, who had returned to the land of his birth just to search for that elusive magic which had gilded the fairy-tale world of his childhood. Tell her that I've been back here seven times in twenty years, and that not until this afternoon when Mr. Riesel, a little Austrian bookseller on the Wollzeile in Vienna, gave you a sales spiel about this book did I *at last* feel really justified for having bothered to come back here at all. So, a merry Christmas to you and to your daughter, Mr. Petersen, and to you, Mr. Riesel, *fröhliche Weihnachten und ein glückliches, neues Jahr!*"

CHAPTER TWELVE

For winter's rains and ruins are over,
And all the season of snows and sins;
The days dividing lover and lover,
The light that loses, the night that wins;
And time remembered is grief forgotten,
And frosts are slain and flowers begotten,
And in green underwood and cover
Blossom by blossom the spring begins. . . .

And Pan by noon and Bacchus by night,
Fleeter of foot than the fleet-foot kid,
Follows with dancing and fills with delight
The Maenad and the Bassarid;
And soft as lips that laugh and hide,
The laughing leaves of the trees divide,

And screen from seeing and leave in sight
The god pursuing, the maiden hid.

The ivy falls with the Bacchanal's hair
Over her eyebrows hiding her eyes;
The wild vine slipping down leaves bare
Her bright breast shortening into sighs;
The wild vine slips with the weight of its leaves,
But the berried ivy catches and cleaves
To the limbs that glitter, the feet that scare
The wolf that follows, the fawn that flies.

I am quoting in orderly, if somewhat willful, sequence these lovely verses from *Atalanta in Calydon*, by Algernon Charles Swinburne, because I was suddenly reminded of them last evening while Margie and I were watching the Miss Universe contest, which was being nationally broadcast from Miami Beach.

If all this seems like the ultimate *non sequitur* of explanations, then let me quickly give you the clue to my really not so far-fetched associative ramblings. You see, the pagan festivals of classic antiquity surely served as cathartic purgations for the common man, who was seasonally privileged to indulge in certain ritualistically authorized excesses for the sake of keeping him in reasonable order during the rest of the year. I have no doubt that our somewhat less exciting, and perhaps even rather torpid annual festivities to pick Miss America or Miss Universe are just bowdlerized hangovers from those more frankly orgiastic times. Of course, our spectacularly arid and, I might even say, antiseptic, ceremonies are certainly guaranteed to smother any possible inclinations of a saturnalian character in anyone excepting, perhaps, in a chronically afflicted case of priapism.

Even so, the inevitable parade of scantily bathing suited damsels proves that some persistently altruistic backstage maneuverer still cherishes the wild notion that these almost vegetarian displays of fleshly temptations might, somehow, come to rouse a remnant of buoyancy in a public which seems to have completely lost its ancient faculties for any sort of joyous, animalistic playfulness.

And that is why I insist that the spirit of the Greeks, who "clashed cymbals on Naxos," continues to live on in our fearfully overcommercialized society and that our Miss Americas and our Miss Universes are just the expurgated versions of those early aphroditic handmaidens who evoked wild public enthusiasm and, incidentally, helped to inspire the sculptors and the poets of twenty-five hundred years ago to create some of their immortal masterpieces.

Naturally, there is something particularly revealing and not a little depressing in the fact that all of the young women who are thus dished up to us, for our special delectation, should be wearing the identical, internationally false, eyelashes. Also, the sundry sponsors who foot the bills for these displays insist on constantly reminding us that without their soaps, their hair lotions, their various skin creams, unguents, depilatories, bath oils and underarm rectifiers, these girls would all be a lot of undistinguished nobodies. It is clearly implied, if not actually stated, that if any or all of their highly touted cosmetic preparations should be consistently ignored, then—curls will begin to droop, bosoms proceed to sag, eyebrows tend to shag up like frayed bottle brushes, and all of these erstwhile Queens of Beauty will be doomed to sink back into the roles of just Common Drabs.

Moving very purposefully behind all these spectacles arranged to exalt female loveliness, there stand the manufacturers of hair tamers, the manufacturers of bosom controllers, the manufacturers of eyelash improvers—and so on. Well, just for the hell of it, I'd someday like to see the people who actually manufactured the *girls*. I mean the fathers and mothers who, mostly without guidance or supervision from anybody, managed to turn out such a high-class product. I want the respective parents of all these thrice-blessed maidens to be trotted out in pairs, right after each of their labeled creations is bowing, in all directions, to acknowledge her public acclaim. I would derive great comfort from such an arrangement because it would certify to me that these distinguished prizewinners had all been really projected into the world by *live* men and women and not just by a lot of slick-looking IBM machines. I say bring on the natural begetters of all this pulchritude and, just for a change, let's give *them* a great big hand, too.

I'm tempted to be a little funny about all this, because, essentially, these hideous tableaux always have a strong tendency to get me down. The Beauty Queens and the Kumquat Queens and the Floor-Wax Queens and all the rest of that commercial royalty just give me the aching whim-whams and the galloping heebie-jeebies. It's all been going on for quite a long while too, and it is surely getting worse every day. Even I once got to know a couple of these exalted personages face to face. Yes, I once met Miss Daytona Beach, and a little over twenty years ago I became quite friendly with a girl who was *The Liebert's Piccalilli Queen.* This happened out in Chicago. Her name was Mona Brettschneider, so, naturally, she was officially billed as *Myrna Britt, the Spice of Liebert's Piccalilli.* She happened to live just a couple of doors down the hall from me in the hotel where I was staying, and in one of her less public moments she knocked on my door and asked me for the loan of a calendar.

Let me tell you at once that I'm willing to swear with my dying breath that this desperately mixed up child—she was a little less than seventeen at the time—had originally had the makings of a decent, happy, and altogether wholesome little body—until that ton of prize crap fell down on her, of course. That piece of luck really sent her sprawling.

You see, in those days it was still a complete free-for-all; that is to say, mobs of loafers from nearby pool halls used to just mosey up to this kid's room and start verifying her most vital statistics with tape measures. They'd say they were newspapermen, or art experts, or whatever the hell happened to come into their minds, and Myrna was just simple enough to let those *momsers* get away with it.

I tried to wise her up, but she was already too far gone with booze and sleeping around and everything, and only a few years later, when I saw her again in New York, did she give me the lowdown on the whole bloody farce. "I just didn't really know what was happening to me," she said. "All I can tell you is that I was an honest-to-John virgin when I first landed in Chicago and, before I knew it, every loose louse in that stinking town was crawling all over me. I sure was right in the middle of it when I first met you, and, about a month after you left, I finally landed in a hospital. I had an abortion that was badly botched, and after I got over that I landed in a psychiatric ward. Those damned piccalilli people, the Lieberts, wanted to have nothing to do with me, of course. They'd originally given me a hundred dollars cash and the two-week trip to Chicago. Some clothing store in my hometown gave me an evening dress worth about twenty-five dollars; I got my hair and my nails done for nothing, and some other big shot back in Lansingville fixed me up with some gloves, some shoes, and a lot of black lace underwear. They told me I'd earn a fortune before the year was out and that I was sure to get a screen test in a big Hollywood studio. Well, when the year was out I was in the booby hatch and my poor mother had to sell her house to get me proper medical treatment and to pay for my long convalescence. Believe *me*, that was *some* experience. I wouldn't wish such a thing on my worst enemy."

A great many merchandise and/or produce queens had a pretty crazy time of it there for quite a long while, and the biggest come-on of all was the constantly promised screen test that was just hovering right over the horizon. Do you know, if ever any of these misguided schnooks actually managed to land in Hollywood (generally by prearrangement with some boozed-up movie press agent), half the stagehands at the studio had already slept with her before she'd even had a chance to meet a third assistant director's dumb, blond secretary. It was just awful.

That's why the smart boys in the advertising racket decided to change the whole setup.

Nowadays the girls are chaperoned more closely than if they lived in a convent. Day and night somebody hovers over them and sees to it that no unauthorized satchel-bum can get anywhere near them.

Don't you see? These girls have come to be identified with—and to some extent they even symbolize—the *Purity of the Sponsor's Product*. You can believe me that *that* is the purity which really *counts*. That is the purity which is backed by millions of dollars, and this priceless ingredient is certainly not going to get slopped up by any sluttish or tramplike behavior on the part of any of the official contestants.

That is, surely, all to the good.

Unfortunately, all of these shrewd business precautions have also had a few rather deleterious side effects; they have, for example, given these preposterous ventures a somewhat genderless character. The revolting biddies and biddie-buddies who naturally accumulate around the launchings of such enterprises seem to exude certain eunuchoid vapors, and I believe that these stultifying emanations, finally, tend to embalm all such grotesque charades in an atmosphere of almost clinical sterility.

In the end, you sometimes can't help wondering whether all of these desperately ambitious, synthetic-looking broads actually have about their persons the usual number of bodily apertures that most ordinary girls are generally endowed with.

I personally would hesitate to commit myself on this subject one way or another.

At any rate, as I was thinking about this prize-winning mania, which, like an incurable fever, keeps simmering away in the bloodstream of our contemporary society, it came to me that someone might write a reasonably entertaining musical play on this subject; and since no one has, up to this time, given any signs that he was contemplating such a venture, I will submit to you a brief outline along this general theme and let it rest there, until some better-qualified person comes along to do the job up real brown.

The name of this musical should be "Winners All!" You see, I have imagined it somewhere along these lines:

The action takes place in a large, well-equipped and altogether up-to-date sanitarium. Individual treatments, group therapy, psychodrama and the very latest miracle drugs are available to the clientele. This institution, called *Finisterre*, is run by an idealistic psychiatrist whose name is Othon Langbreit and whose large staff of assistants and nurses simply idolizes him.

This institution treats only very special cases and, over a period of time, the management has developed uniquely suitable methods of therapy to cope with some rather unusual forms of psychic disorder.

It seems that Dr. Langbreit has discovered a number of effective techniques for the treatment of people who have suffered deep emotional disturbances because they were always only runners-up and never the actual winners in various prize contests.

He has made a long and thorough study of this malaise, and, fortunately, certain sufficient funds have been allotted to his institution, which makes it possible for him to carry on his work practically on a scholarship basis. I think it is altogether reasonable to assume that characters who land in such a place don't have very much money to spare. It is just because they are constantly on the outer borders of penury that they participate in a lot of contests in the first place. They expect to make it from a beat-up Chevrolet to a brand-new Cadillac in one wild somersault, assisted by nothing more tangible than just a totally befuddled queen of destiny.

Well, then, let us decide once and for all that Dr. Langbreit is the unchallenged (and not the runner-up) authority in this particular area of psychiatric disaster.

There will be about thirteen or, maybe, fifteen roles to fill, but at least half of them can be played by actors who are sufficiently skilled to double up in some of the minor parts.

The people who have come here for treatment have not always been total failures in their competitive endeavors. Many of them have achieved minor triumphs in various hotly contested fields on local and even national levels. They possess numberless small trophies acquired in a great diversity of activities, but, unfortunately, not one of them ever quite managed to make it into the absolute big time. That, indeed, is their hang-up.

Allow me to indicate just a few of our protagonists:

One of the female patients is Belle Sauvage, aged twenty-two; she was runner-up to *Miss Bayou Blossom of Louisiana, 1959.*

Then we have Mr. Dino Waller, aged twenty, who ran second to the *Coronado Beach Boy of the Year* in 1961.

Another lady is Tina Elmlight, aged twenty-five, who nearly became *Miss Cornstarch of Winenga, Ohio,* in 1960.

Also present is John Firkin, aged twenty-five, who nearly landed the title *Mazda Lamp Salesman of South Winnetka* in 1958.

Anyway, this will give you an idea of what is going on.

However, I must not forget to mention the Altobergi twins, Suzanne and Celeste, who were almost chosen to perform in a famous Doublemint chewing-gum commercial on TV, when Celeste suddenly caught the mumps and stopped resembling anybody, including her sister. Suzanne finally did manage to catch it, too, but that was just ten days after the sponsor had signed up another set of identical twins, who had even been born in Siam. Celeste and Suzanne haven't spoken a single word to each other in over three years.

There are other patients around, of course—mostly middle-aged and quite cantankerous elderly characters. These people have been hopelessly frustrated because they won only honorable mentions even though they had correctly filled out certain newspaper quiz diagrams, in which the faces of a dozen infants had been cunningly concealed in the lush foliage of a pen-and-ink yohimbé tree. Three or four other moody ones achieved only prizes of ball-point pens although they had meticulously outlined, with ball-point pens, the greatest possible number of bunny rabbits that had been hidden by the artist in a cartoon drawing of a Louisiana briar patch.

In short, everybody has a damned good reason to be on the wall.

Each patient carries several books or boxes of clippings and will, on the slightest provocation, proceed to quote from them.

These quotes will be sung, of course. For instance:

John Firkin is like a young Gable;
Better keep an eye on him.
He's star material and very able;
You can watch him in the YMCA gym.

Tom Nessbitt in the Massachusetts Bugle

or:

Little Tina Elmlight is always bright and gay,
I'm sure she's bound for Hollywood
Or maybe old Broadway.
Our little Tina Elmlight, I'm sure she will go far;
Such beauty and such talent
Will make her into a star.
It's a shame to see her in the Bijou dime store,
When she should be where the big chances are.

Thelma Vorsprung in the Sedalia Banner

And so on. Among the doctors, I fancy Dr. Louis Lippert as the hero. He is thirty-five years old and serves as Dr. Langbreit's first assistant, and he is secretly in love with Langbreit's seventeen-year-old daughter, whom you haven't met yet.

Her name is June, and since her mother—two years previously—ran off with one of the patients (a rehabilitated schizophrenic who inherited a castle totally bereft of plumbing, in the north of Wales), this young girl has really had no proper parental supervision. There is an old European saying that "The shoemaker's children generally go barefoot." It certainly applies in this case, because Dr. Langbreit, who spends all his time curing other people of their manias, has failed to notice that his own daughter is really off her rocker. In his desire to retard her maturity, he dresses her in childish pinafores, but it is obvious to everyone, excepting the head psychiatrist, that June is busting out all over.

So the plot goes something like this: Dr. Lippert is trying to persuade June to marry him, but she nixes it because she wants to become something sensational. She is tired of the sanitarium and plans to have a career on television or in the movies or both. She scorns Lippert's offer and taunts him with his measly earnings as a headshrinker. She wants a real American career. Everything about the sanitarium's medical staff has overtones of Freud's old Austria. It makes her absolutely sick. She is secretly training for the Miss America contest out in Atlantic City, and that's why she's up every day at sunrise to do roadwork. She's learning to sew her own dresses, too, and one of the patients, a Miss Tallahassee (runner-up), is giving her instructions in proper ways of walking and in speaking extemporaneously. As a matter of fact, June has her special evening gown all ready and is only waiting for the occasion to display all her long-hidden goodies. Poor Lippert is completely staggered by these disclosures. He wrestles with his conscience, or whatever the hell a psychiatrist uses for a conscience, whether he ought to apprise his chief about all these sinister goings-on or whether he ought to just permanently dump all this dangerous fallout into the murky regions of his subconscious. While he and his superego are on the mat with this problem, an absolutely sanitarium-shaking event takes place.

A patient arrives who was once an actual top winner at *something*. She was once crowned queen of *Nelson's Full-Flavored Apple Butter*—Miss Thelma Brazière of Chinnacook, Washington. That anyone who had actually made it in the big leagues should, nevertheless, have somehow managed to flip her tortillas causes endless excitement among all those damaged entities, and even the supervisory ensemble is in quite a dither about this strange case.

It looks, at this point, as if I'm being so totally carried away by the dizzy momentum of my plot that I seem to have made no allowances at all for suitable music and proper lyrics. Well, we can have a masquerade ball somewhere in the show, to which everybody in the joint comes dressed as the person he would really like to be. On this occasion the medical staff, led by our hero, Dr. Lippert, can sing a song something like this:

Both doctors and laymen are quite agreed
That meaningless leisure is stifling.
A creative hobby is what all men need,
No matter how simple and trifling.
But sad to relate is the actual state
Of the subject on which we're reporting:
Too many are settling their whole earthly fate
On the trifle that should be just sporting.
Oh, it's fine to have a hobby when life is too static,
For idleness breeds discontent.
Raise rabbits in your cellar or mushrooms in your attic,
But please don't make a mess of Nature's natural intent.
Remember, it is love that makes the world go round,
And the destiny that all of us must face
Is to carry the ball as we're all duty-bound
And to continue the great human race.

Oh, it's better far to mate than sublimate,
For there isn't any substitute for life.
Oh, it's better far to mate than sublimate,
So just try to be a husband or a wife.
If you shudder at the thought of procreation,
And you'd rise above your instincts through creation,
If your gender's just a part-time filling station,
You will find a foolish vain thing
Is your cosmic abstract painting
When it comes to face the sexual equation.
So if it's not too late, then be prepared to meet your fate,
For it's better far to mate than sublimate.

Oh, it's better far to mate than sublimate,
Or you'll wind up as a misanthropic grouch.
Oh, it's better far to mate than sublimate

And risk the psychoanalytic couch.
You will just collect dishonorable mentions
If you're violating nature's prime intentions
With some novel subumbilical inventions.
Think of Sodom and Gomorrah
Where, to prehistoric horror,
They just flouted all society's conventions.
So if it's not too late, then be a man and face your fate,
For it's better far to mate than sublimate.

Of course, I'm not a lyric writer, and the whole thing will eventually have to be handled by experts. I just wanted to give a few hints and indicate along what lines the general thematic material might be most successfully exploited.

Finally, I suppose I'll have to introduce you to the villain of the piece. I'm a little mixed up about him at the moment, because my mind is divided between two people whom I had figured as possibilities for this role. At first I thought of having him come on as a slick-looking drug salesman—you know, the kind of a guy who carries a lot of free samples in his attaché case and is forever bombarding the medical profession with new antibiotics and cortisone derivatives. I thought I'd have this character start the notion going that all of the clinics and sanitariums in the land ought to hold a beauty contest for their best-looking patients. Before you start sniggering at such an absurd idea, you'd better take a look in today's paper, because before you know it that kind of competition will probably be under way.

Well, this beauty-contest thing is quite all right with all of the other places around the country, but at *Finisterre*, which is full up with fractured egos who have come to grief right along that selfsame route, this proposition, naturally, causes the most profound apprehensions. I must say I like this particular twist in the plot, but I had another fellow in mind who might have promulgated the same crisis—and, what's more, he himself is a patient at the Langbreit clinic.

This man, whose name is Alfie Remick, had flunked out at one hundred and twenty-eight dollars from the *Sixty-Four-Thousand-Dollar Question* program some years ago, and at the very beginning of the play we would discover that he is also deeply enamored of June Langbreit. This emotional involvement could apply to the drug salesman, too, but I think it might prove particularly poignant if the moving force of evil originated intramurally, at the institution itself. However, I'll leave all that suspended for the moment.

At any rate, this Remick character is the most irreconcilably bitter man in the place, because he is actually a very well informed man and probably the topmost living authority on the subject of tropical fish (which had been his chosen category on the now-defunct TV show).

You see, he really *knew* all of the answers, up to the very toughest one, worth two hundred and fifty-six thousand dollars, but he had been persuaded, or, better still, he had been browbeaten into deliberately fluffing his answer to make way for a more photogenic, more humanly appealing contestant named Bernard Flutter. This Flutter person also lost out—that very same evening, as a matter of fact—not because anybody had coached him to do so but because he was just naturally very stupid. He is now a fellow patient at the institution, too, and, what's more, these two people happen to be the very best of friends.

I think, so far, everything is pretty tidy in our story, and I've even got a smashing second-act curtain all ready for you.

It takes place at the masquerade ball, of course, where everybody is dressed up as his own ideal. Costumewise, it is a very simple problem, really, since all of the women are blondes in bouffant evening gowns and their faces are covered by identical masks. Each of these ladies wears false eyelashes two inches long, and the hypnotic grin which is permanently frozen onto each face discloses at least sixty-four teeth of an absolutely blinding, neon-illuminated iridescence.

June, wearing her own homemade creation, is, of course, lost in this bevy of anonymous horrors, but Dr. Lippert, with the unerring instincts of love, approaches her for a dance. She scorns him and is just about to give him a long look at her free-form shoulder blades when a perspiring messenger suddenly breaks upon the festivities and makes an announcement which is unmatched among second-act curtains.

The newcomer is Ferdinand Schlepperturm, an old retainer of Dr. Langbreit's from his student days in Klosterneuburg, and as he desperately tries to control his breath he finally stammers out the following:

"They've just counted the money in the glass barrel in the Rexall drugstore over at Springfield, and the barrel contained two hundred and eighty-three thousand dollars and sixty-two cents."

The whole assembly of masqueraders is stunned into silence.

Dr. Langbreit, dressed as Dante Alighieri, comes forward and puts a quieting hand on Schlepperturm's heaving chest. "I'm sorry, Schlepperturm," he says, "but you don't seem to realize that we have a little party going on here."

Schlepperturm looks the doctor straight in the eye and says, "I just thought you might want to know that that barrel of money has been in that drugstore window for the past six weeks and it was announced in all the papers that whoever came closest to guessing the real amount that was inside that barrel would collect all of the money."

Everyone moves closer. A hum of excitement thick enough to cut with a butter knife rises from the assembled throng as Dr. Langbreit says, "You must take a lukewarm bath and a lemonade without sugar, Schlepperturm, and then go to bed with the window raised."

Schlepperturm, like a man in a trance, seems not even to have heard the doctor's gratuitous medical advice. In fact, he now turns away from his old patron and, looking straight at June Langbreit, says clearly but with his usual lisp, "The winner of all that money is the man whose guess was so close that he missed by only thirty-one cents."

121

"Yes! Yes! Yes!" screams the electrified crowd. "And who *is* the man?!?!?"

"This winner," says Schlepperturm, as his voice becomes rich, like a well-made Bostom clam chowder, "this winner is—*Dr. Louis Lippert of Finisterre!*"

Well, you can just imagine the racket. Most of the people in that crowd, who have been chronic losers all of their lives, would now become completely deranged if it hadn't already happened some time ago. Mobs are milling around Dr. Lippert, who, grim-visaged and ashen-faced, looks straight at June Langbreit, who stands alone, in her homemade bouffant, like a cupcake that someone has locked out on the window ledge. We hold this picture for a full sixty seconds and we also continue with the mob's incoherent hubbub—until the curtain slowly descends on Act Two.

And, now, what is left for Act Three? A great deal, friends. First of all, the patients have gotten wind of the impending inter-sanitarium beauty contest. This is a chance for them to practice their songs of acknowledgment in case they should *win*. I haven't really given much thought to these lyrics, but something along this general direction might give you a clue:

I'm the Queen of Ill Health
And I don't owe to wealth
My position of su-pre-ma-cee.
So, bring on your sedation
And let's tell the nation
About psycho-thera-pee.
Ra-pee—!
Good old psycho-thera-pee!

Oh, they boast of their hair
And their skin that is fair
And the blemishless state of their form;
But my claim to fame is more firmly entrenched,
And the crown of uniqueness I hold firmly clenched,
Since I'm way the hell out from the norm.

122

As a matter of fact, you could have several subdivisions in the various main categories of mental disturbance and perhaps go even farther and have a Miss-Anthropy, a Miss-Cegenation, a Miss-Carriage, and so on. In the end *everybody* would wind up with a prize, and then a mixed chorus might sing:

We've won speedboats and cars,
Soda fountains and bars,
And the things for which every heart wishes;
Tra-la-lee, tra-la-la.
A litter of St. Bernard pups,
A life supply of Dixie cups,
And eight thousand hand-painted dishes.
Tra-la-lee, tra-la-la.

Oh, we've been on the heights
And we know the delights
When the whole world is grander than grand.
We've won carloads of Cokes,
Endless cartons of smokes,
And free passes to see Disneyland.
Tra-la-lee, tra-la-la (etc.).

As for the final solution of the plot, it is really quite simple. At a staff meeting, Dr. Lippert offers to turn his winnings over to The Finisterre Defrustration Fund. He proposes that they abandon their old therapeutic methods and devote all their energies, henceforth, to winning prizes and to running supervisory seminars for people who want to compete in various prize contests.

"I can say without immodesty that I have a certain knack in that direction myself," says Dr. Lippert. "And since this acute competitive condition is surely not just a passing phase in our civilization, I propose that we learn to *live* with it rationally. Acceptance of an irremediable situation is the first step to sanity."

He also points out that since the arrival of the *Apple Butter*

Queen a wave of wholesome reassurance has come over all of their patients. "Of course, they are still very far from sane," says Dr. Lippert, "but only a technically trained expert could tell them apart from ordinary people. Miss Brazière, on the other hand, has found herself so much comforted by her daily contacts with these amiable losers that she, in her turn, is practically ready to be discharged as cured."

Further, it is resolved with the unanimous approval of the entire clinical faculty that all contestants in need of help are to be charged only minimal fees for institutional guidance but are to be under contractual obligation to turn twenty-five percent of their winnings, if any, over to The Finisterre Defrustration Fund, Inc.

In the end, after Dr. Lippert has consented that June should instantly begin training for the next *Mrs.* America contest, she agrees to marry him at once. Since everyone in the sanitarium has noticed that Miss Brazière is more than just superficially devoted to Dr. Langbreit, it is inevitable, before too long, that this distinguished savant finally also catches wise to his fortunate condition.

In fact, just before the last curtain descends, it might be a hell of an idea to hold a double wedding—a plot situation which has been sadly lacking in our theater ever since the Dolly Sisters made their last appearance on Broadway.

Of course, I haven't been able to give time to a lot of incidental business that can easily take place around an institution of that sort. For instance, when two total strangers meet for the first time, they could bow to one another and proceed to introduce themselves by having one of them say, "Victor Kimmel, manic-depressive," and having the other one reply, "Donald Prellnick, acute alcoholic," after which they would solemnly shake hands.

If all of the patients do this, it will spare us the necessity for a great deal of boring exposition. The audience will know what's wrong with everybody in the joint in just two minutes flat.

I really think the possibilities are absolutely unlimited.

CHAPTER THIRTEEN

S INCE I'VE HAD a lifelong love affair with world literature, I decided some time ago to include in this final volume of my autobiography a number of pivotal excerpts out of those books which have had the deepest impact on my consciousness. I meant to comment briefly, and yet elucidatively, on the reasons why these particular works of art had achieved their unique status in the awareness of all cultivated peoples. In addition, it was my intention to give the intellectual and emotional causes for my own peculiar involvement with these significant creations.

Unfortunately, after finishing my first outline for this project, it became clear to me that this whole idea, although possibly a very useful one, would surely take up nearly a thousand pages, even if I decided to cover just the barest essentials of my general intentions.

So that was out.

I consoled myself with the thought that during almost every

Christmas season many of the book-review sections of our large metropolitan newspapers publish several columns of what are sometimes called Basic Reading Lists for Adults. I have collected about half a dozen of such pieces in the past decade, and I think Clifton Fadiman's Baedeker of titles through worthwhile literature, printed in the New York *Times* several seasons ago, is about as succinct a guide as anyone could possibly desire. Besides, I am only too well aware that for a great many people the mere *possession* of such a list gives the *possessor* an automatic sense of accomplishment—so much so, in fact, that he generally doesn't have to do another damned thing more about it.

So I will have to content myself by giving you four or five small teasers from out of the vast quantity of meaningful reading matter which has passed through my hands during the last half century. That is to say, later on in these pages I will try to illuminate with a few personal footnotes some aspects of literature which, as far as I know, never get on *anybody's* reading lists. You see, just because I have, for so long a time, done such an enormous amount of consistent reading, I have finally arrived at a point where I have developed a great liking for those shady rivulets of ink which hardly ever manage to reach the mainstream of general attention at all. For the past few years I have immersed myself almost exclusively in the letters and intimate diaries of the world's distinguished artists and authors, and in many instances I have found myself even closer to the heartbeats of their creative urgencies and triumphs than when I first perused their officially acknowledged masterpieces.

For the moment, however, I would like to say something to you about my discovery of Heinrich Heine. I first found him in a bookshop in Vienna when I was—in years—just a child. I had read much of Goethe, Schiller, Freiligrath, Wolfram von Eschenbach and even somebody called Hoffmann von Fallersleben, since their writings formed part of every normal school curriculum. Hölderlin I had also discovered for myself, and, when I finally stumbled upon Heine, it seemed to me as if I had at last found a long-lost spiritual brother whose genius had voiced, and often very effectively realized, a great many of my own earthbound aspirations. His poems, a goodly number of which had been set to music by some of the greatest melodic masters of all time, became for me a treasure-house which I never wearied of exploring; but his prose works—*Die Harzreise die Bäder von Lucca, Florentinische Nächte, Der Rabbi von Bachrach*—his many fanciful and satirical essays, and even his sometimes quite dated polemical writings eventually became the basic literary staples for my entire adolescence. I suffered ecstasies of perception as I quoted and translated him freely to all my friends, and there are people still of my acquaintance who remember my youthful infatuation with Heine to this very day.

I indulged myself in the belief that a great emotional and intellectual kinship existed between him and myself, and this piece of teen-age presumption will more readily be pardoned when you consider that I was an only child, a stranger in a new land, one who was often compelled to seek most of his comforts and consolations in the pages of books.

I think it was Joseph Delteil who, when challenged by someone for giving too much supposedly authoritative information on the rather intimate thought processes of Napoleon Bonaparte, said, "I know exactly what Napoleon thought because I *am* Napoleon!"

Well, that's just about how I finally came to feel about Heinrich Heine.

Some chapters back I mentioned to you that my Hungarian friend Nandor had recalled a time in our childhood when, as the result of some pretty reckless gastronomical indulgences, both of us had become bedridden and how, in the course of our recovery, I had told him one of Heinrich Heine's youthful reminiscences. I will tell this story to you now, because I have never found an even halfway satisfactory version of it in English. Actually, it is no story at all; it is merely a tiny fraction from his fragment of an autobiography, and it happens to be particularly dear to me because I cherish everything which has even the slightest factual bearing upon his life. When I say *factual*, I mean that he mentions the names of people who lived in Düsseldorf during his childhood and adolescence, and I can tell you that in Europe it was never possible to mislay *real* people. To every person born in the Old Country a vast collection of written statistical trivia was eventually bound to accrue, and so it was possible, during the past century, for earnest scholars to authenticate the basic statistics of the various personalities referred to in Heine's tales. The dossiers of these people formed the public records of the town, and the only matters not mentioned in those frayed and speckled pages were the things which are of most significance in the lines which follow.

Heine was born in Düsseldorf at the end of the eighteenth century. Germany at that time was composed of an infinite number of little kingdoms and principalities, each of them equipped with an Exalted Highness of sorts who surrounded himself with a miniature court, whose like, in all its decorative stiltedness, can, even now, be quite successfully evoked from the painted tops of a few still-available old snuffboxes. Curiously enough, some of these single-eyeglassed, rather Frenchified *serenissimi* weren't always complete numskulls either, since the Duke of Weimar, for instance, had the excellent good sense to secure Goethe as his court philosopher. It was a powdered, periwigged, spinet-tinkling time, in which parochial night watchmen, equipped with pikes and lanterns, still chanted the hours as they passed into eternity.

It was also a period in which an emerging middle class of solid burghers was beginning to imitate both the manners and the costumes of a rather febrile aristocracy. Of course, there were still a good many medieval hangovers festering away at the undercrust of this society, and Heine, with his occasionally bizarre taste for certain gothic orientations of mind, loved to delve into those shadowy corners of the community ethos in which palliative fetishisms and every imaginable sort of black superstition were still holding out against the searching rays disseminated by the golden splendors of the Age of Reason.

One more point: in Heine's day, capital crimes were punished either by hanging or, depending on the nature of the mayhem that had been perpetrated, by decapitation with a large, two-edged sword.

So much for the general setting, and now here is his memoir:

When I was sixteen years old I used to spend a good deal of my idle time at the home of an elderly female commonly called Die Meisterin. Actually she was the widow of the local hangman, and it was believed that her husband had, over the years, initiated this elaborately pockmarked but otherwise extremely self-assured female into many of the arcane rituals connected with his macabre profession. After his demise she became the unofficial sorceress of the town and dealt rather profitably in philters of varied aims and potencies as well as sundry esoteric tokens to ward off the evil eye. I knew for a fact that she did a particularly lucrative business in selling the amputated fingers of certain unfortunate malefactors who had been executed during her husband's tenure of office. She seemed to have an almost unlimited supply of these sinister tokens hidden away in some briny substance down in the stony confines of her dank cellar. Indeed, I once accidentally overheard her telling one of her prospective customers that the fingers of an innocently condemned man were infinitely more potent in their salubrious propensities than those of a guilty one.

To confess the truth, the magnet which drew me so consistently to the home of this ogre was activated not so much by my innate taste for the gruesome; it was rather that I had become the victim of a form of hexing against which there isn't really much help: you see, Die Meisterin had a young niece living with her whose name was Josepha and who was exactly of my own age.

Josepha, or Sefi, as people used to call her, had landed in our town because her father, who had been Die Meisterin's brother, had died some time before. He had also been a hangman, and since he was a widower when death came to him, the orphaned little girl had been taken in by her maternal grandfather, who served as the county executioner for all of Westphalia. After five years he, too, went on to his unknown reward, and it was then that Die Meisterin finally decided to incorporate her young niece into her highly peculiar household.

What can I tell you about Josepha?

She had grown prematurely tall and, hence, very slender, and yet there was about her sweet awkwardness a certain precocious and even voluptuous femininity. Since she wore neither a corset nor half a dozen petticoats, her close-fitting garments gave her a startling resemblance to a moistly draped statue. But no marble statue ever carved by man could compete with the multiple facets of her breathtaking loveliness. Each of her movements was like the subtle development in some fabulously integrated musical composition. Not a single one of Niobe's daughters ever bore a countenance of nobler proportions, and the color of her skin was like a constantly altering resonance on a theme of purest white. Her large, dark eyes looked as if they had given the world a rather complex riddle to decipher and were now expectantly waiting for their long-delayed answer. Her mouth, which she had endeavored to compress into a line of contemptuous thinness, had escaped her will and had finally managed to swell into its own sensuous perfection.

Her hair was red—a wild, wild red—and she generally had it hanging in carelessly disordered ringlets down along her wonderfully articulated shoulder blades. The one thing I found disturbing about Sefi was her voice. This voice had a curiously veiled sound, a sound without any real timbre, and only when she grew angry did a certain curiously metallic tone emanate from that throat of hers—and this was the very thing which was particularly upsetting for me, since I recognized with a profound shock that, on these extreme occasions, her voice was like an exact echo of my own. It was a truly frightening experience for me to listen to her, and the nightmarish quality of that sound was something I found positively unnerving.

Sefi knew a great number of ancient folk songs, and I can easily account for the strange quality of my early poems—"The Dream Pictures," for instance—on the basis of her potent influence over my imagination during those highly impressionable years of my life.

Among the superannuated chanteys which she frequently sang for me, there was one short, rhymed ditty which I have never been able to find in any collection of folk music or folk verse, although I have searched for it diligently in many places over quite a long period of time. It goes like this. At first an evil spirit, called Tragig, is speaking:

Otilje love, Otilje dear,
You're surely not the last one here.
Speak! Would you hang from the high, high tree?
Or would you swim in the deep, blue sea?
Or would you kiss the sword's cold steel
Which God has destined for you to feel?

To which Otilje answers:

I will not hang from the high, high tree,
I will not swim in the deep, blue sea,
I will rather kiss the sword's cold steel,
Which God has destined for me to feel.

It may well seem like a meaningless jingle to you now, but all I can tell you is that once, when Josepha had come to the end of this song, I noticed how unaccountably disturbed she suddenly seemed and I, too, catching the waves of her nameless agitation, was so deeply shaken with sympathy for the state of her emotions that we both fell to weeping convulsively and stared into each other's faces through a veil of unstillable tears.

I begged Sefi to write down the words of that song for me, which she did at once, but not with ink. She penned it with some drops of her own dear blood, and I carried this red holograph manuscript around with me for a great many years. I finally lost it, as I have lost so many other precious things in my life, but, as you see, I never forgot the rhymes.

I have spoken to you about Josepha's past with her father and grandfather, who had both been public excutioners, and I left it to you to surmise the dreadful loneliness of this marked child, who had spent all of her young days in the Freihaus, which was the name by which the home of the hangman was officially designated. Since this house and all of its inhabitants were superstitiously shunned by all the rest of the community, poor Josepha had lacked almost every form of human companionship and from her earliest infancy onward had been completely thrown back upon her own tremulously uncertain resources. It had made her into a painfully sensitive and desperately suspicious creature who was unable to control a visible shudder even if anyone, just accidentally, happened to touch her. By contrast with this shrinking aspect of her nature, she could, on occasion, become absolutely violent and give herself to outbursts of fierce denunciations against persons and injustices which were, in most instances, almost wholly imaginary. Yes, I discovered in due time that something untamable and unpredictable slumbered uneasily beneath Josepha's seemingly most relaxed moods.

Once she confessed to me that she never dreamed about people at all. Her dreams, from earliest childhood on, had always been only of animals.

In the loneliness of her grandfather's proscribed house, a house whose shadow never fell on any passerby, she had busied herself in the deciphering of some dust-covered tomes which, late one Sunday afternoon, she had come upon in a neglected corner of an abandoned storeroom. The old man, who rarely spoke to anyone, had nevertheless troubled himself to teach her reading and writing, and since his gory duties sometimes took him pretty far afield, Josepha spent her time either quite alone or in the company of three doddering females who had, for a great number of years, been keeping the hangman's possessions in a sufficiently tidy state of repair. Her grandfather's home was situated on the fringe of a dense forest, and during the long winter nights when the biting winds exacted painful squeaks and groans from the tortured trunks and branches of the twisted old oak trees, these storm-tossed veterans would sometimes knock their fingers and even their very arms up against the walls of the Freihaus, as if asking for human help against the relentless inclemencies of the weather.

The three crones who had been left in charge of the manse drank a great deal of mulberry brandy, and, while waggling their palsied heads over their spinning wheels, they would interpret the sounds of the night according to their own peculiar dispositions.

However, it was their common conceit that these repeated knockings upon the walls and shutters were actually perpetrated by certain thieves who had but recently been hanged and who begged just for a brief admittance into the warm coziness of the Freihaus. As the snow whirled fitfully around the building they saw, pressed up against the frozen windowpanes, the faces of other executed criminals making pitiful grimaces in the wild hope that their agonies might move the fortunately sheltered householders into making room for them at their own blazing firesides. Sometimes they even heard them screaming their wretched lamentations in so loud a voice that the very howling of the winds seemed muted by the fierce poignancy of their unearthly cries.

The most persistent of these gruesome visitors returned to demand their missing fingers, and these desperate ones could only be driven away if one of the old women would rush off into a nearby storeroom and quickly return bearing one of the swords of execution. Such an instrument seemed to be the most effective means of frightening these errant souls back again upon the high beams of their icicle-encrusted gallows trees.

There were certain occasions when the grandfather, in getting under way the special arrangements for some rather unusual mass executions, would entertain a number of his professional colleagues from the nearby provinces. At such times the festive board actually groaned under the weight of all the rich roasts and rare wines which were served up to the assembled company. Cellars and larders were emptied of their culinary riches, and the guests drank of the most select vintages out of heavy goblets made of pure silver.

You see, if ever a hangman happened to enter a public inn in search of some liquid refreshment, mine host usually served him out of a pewter tankard which was equipped with a special wooden cover. Lacking such furniture, the innkeeper might also serve his guest out of a glass, but it was obligatory on the guest's part to shatter this vessel as soon as the last drop had been drained. This was done so that no other human being might come to drink out of a vessel contaminated by the lips of a public executioner. No one ever spoke to these men, and the money they rendered in payment for any service was usually held over the light of a burning candle and, as an additional measure of precaution, it was later on dipped into a basin of holy water.

But when any of these ostracized men gave entertainment to their own kind, they ate the choicest of foods and the wines they offered one another were poured into goblets made of the rarest metals.

Sefi told me that one day, when she was about eight years old, a great number of guests appeared at her grandfather's home, which was quite surprising, since no special executions seemed to be in the offing at that time. She told me that it had been a day in the late fall of the year when, suddenly, about a dozen men, all of them quite old and some of them even rather feeble, had turned up in their dooryard and had started to cackle at each other in friendly greeting, like chickens who, after a daylong separation, are reunited at eventime in their family coop.

Some of them had ice-gray beards, Josepha told me, and some of them were quite bald, and all of them wore their official executioners' costumes, which meant blood-red capes, with their swords dangling from thick leather straps around their shoulders. Underneath their capes these curious guests wore clothing that had been long out of fashion and, as far as she could understand, they had come together just to "convene."

It turned out later that these were the oldest hangmen still alive at that time and that at least half of them had come for great distances to be present at this particular gathering. They shook hands over and over again, like children who cannot seem to contain their exuberance at a particularly exciting party. Naturally, the finest delicacies of the kitchen were served up to them in a ceaseless chain of extravagantly prepared courses, but, when the sun began to set, the grandfather had every trace of the day's festivity removed and, what is more, he dismissed his servants and his henchmen and admonished them not to return to the Freihaus until the following noon. He also sent the three old women on some obviously contrived mission into the next town, and after they were all gone, he carefully chained the dog inside his kennel and stuffed up the entrance hole with an old horse blanket. Before the servants departed, the grandfather had made them place some dozen bottles of wine and also a tall iron candelabrum atop a round stone table which stood in the center of a semicircle of ancient oak trees.

Finally the old man turned to Sefi and asked her to rinse the large silver bowl whose outer surface was encrusted with dolphins and fanciful sea creatures of all sorts. After the child had performed this service, her grandfather, in a manner of kindness which was not untinged by embarrassment, told her to go instantly to bed and to fasten the shutters of her windows with particular care.

But Josepha was far too curious to follow her grandfather's instructions; instead, she posted herself behind some dense bushes that grew almost in the shadow of the trees and, from this admirably sheltered vantage point, she was able, without any difficulty, to observe all the extraordinary events of that night.

At first the strange visitors, led by her grandfather, marched in pairs toward the stone table and seated themselves in a semicircle on some heavy wooden stumps that might, at some time or other, have served as execution blocks. The floating pine wicks were lit in the candelabrum, and by the light of this flickering illumination the men's deeply graven, stony faces were truly terrifying to behold.

They sat for a time in absolute silence, but after a while it seemed to Josepha that they had begun to murmur some inward prayers. These ended when her grandfather reached out to pour the wine into the silver bowl. He served each man a brimming cup, and when all had been accommodated he addressed them in words which were too softly uttered to carry as far as Sefi's hiding place. In any event, whatever the content of his speech, its effect on the assembled company seemed to be absolutely shattering. At first one of the old men began to drop his tears onto his scarlet robe, and, after a few moments, all of the others at the table began to weep without restraint. It looked to the poor, frightened little girl as if the withered images on a timeworn church façade had suddenly started to shed live tears out of their stony eyes. Josepha told me that she could hear them all sobbing like children. A pale, cloud-veiled moon made her melancholy entrance at this point, and the trembling young interloper, secreted in the dense shadows of the trees, thought that her heart would surely break in its blind pity for these pathetic, sorrow-laden men. One old fellow in particular seemed to be more deeply shaken than any of the others. He wept and wrung his poor bony hands in unconsolable despair, and finally he screamed out in a voice of such acute anguish that even Josepha, secreted behind the bushes, was able to hear him quite clearly.

"O God!" he cried. "O God, you are unjust! O God, this misery lasts much too long! No human soul can carry such a burden! O God, you are unjust! Unjust! Unjust!"

His comrades seemed to have great difficulty in quieting him down, but at last they managed to subdue him and, rocking slowly from side to side on his wooden stump, he continued to whimper like a mortally wounded animal.

At last the members of this frightening conclave arose from their seats and, as if by a whispered command, they unanimously doffed their blood-red capes. They again fell into line formation and, two by two, each carrying his sword of office, they approached the largest of the trees, against whose trunk someone, probably earlier in the evening, had placed a large spade.

It was most curious to see with what speed and dexterity one of these frail-looking men managed to dig quite a deep hole. He dug it between the high root shanks of the tallest oak, and when the work was completed her grandfather, who was the only one who had not removed his official cape, produced from the inside folds of this garment a long white package. Bending carefully over the newly dug grave, the old man lowered his ominous parcel tenderly into the ground. The moment it had disappeared from view he proceeded most vigorously to shovel all the loose earth which had accumulated about the place back into the hole again. After this was done, he and his comrades, in order to re-establish the evenness of the sod, proceeded to stamp about in the light of that pallid moon as if they had been just so many spectral dancers clamoring for readmission into their more familiar netherworld.

Well, I suppose poor Josepha had by this time seen about as much as she had wished to see, because when the midnight ballet of the hangmen reached its climactic frenzy she leaped from her hiding place and ran like one by Furies pursued toward the promised haven of her bedchamber.

The next morning, when she awoke, the whole fantastic episode seemed just like a dream to her, but when she had a moment's chance to reconnoiter under the trees, the freshly stamped ground gave clear evidence that everything she remembered had actually taken place. She pondered long and she wondered greatly, particularly about what sort of person or thing could possibly lie buried out there in that newly made grave. Was it a child? An animal? Or perhaps a treasure? She said nothing about her lurid adventure to anyone, and as time passed, it all finally faded into the background of her thoughts.

But five years later, when her grandfather died and Die Meisterin came along to take her into friendly custody, she told her aunt exactly what she had witnessed in the light of that cloud-veiled moon.

I understand that Die Meisterin was neither frightened nor particularly astonished when she heard Josepha's disclosures, and she assured her niece at once that neither child nor cat nor treasure trove lay buried in the shadow of the old oak tree. Actually, that extraordinary woman seemed rather delighted with Sefi's story and told her that the object which had been interred on that memorable night had been nothing more than just her grandfather's official sword. She explained to Sefi that generally, after one hundred poor sinners had been expedited into the beyond by means of such a weapon, it was considered proper and politic in hangmen's circles to give this instrument a formal burial. It was believed to be in the best interest of all concerned that these particular punitive objects be permanently removed from further human contact, since a spirit of seemingly unquenchable bloodthirstiness was often manifested in swords which had been so frequently employed. It was as if these things forged of nothing but cold steel did, after a time, develop a secret awareness of their own sinister usage and finally required to be put to rest and placed into a grave like any human creature that had fulfilled its marked destiny.

Also, it was believed by many that these weapons, after having shed such vast quantities of blood, would often grow quite restless and tend to make a willful clatter in the closets where they had been stored along with other instruments of execution. There were even some who held that they were likely to become quite treacherous and do a world of surprising damage to the very people who had for years seen most meticulously to their welfare.

In fact, her aunt had once confided to Josepha that, in her own family, one of her brothers had stabbed to death his much-loved younger sibling with a sword which had had something well over a hundred executions upon its record.

Nevertheless, this business-minded sorceress proceeded at once to dig up this gruesome instrument, for, she argued, that much-potent magic might perhaps still be evoked through proper conjurations over its highly knowing blade.

Josepha told me that, in fact, her aunt still kept it, along with a great many other instruments connected with her varied acts of necromancy, in the storage room of the very house they then occupied.

One day, when Die Meisterin was away from home, I begged Sefi to show me this resurrected veteran of destruction. I did not have to plead with her overmuch, and without any visible misgivings she left the room and, a moment later, returned carrying an enormous sword of a rather antique order of design. It was of real wonder to me how easily her thin arms managed to support this heavy object, and, as she waved it about and, finally, pointed it directly at my person, she suddenly began to chant in an astonishing, playful manner:

> *Or would you kiss the sword's cold steel*
> *Which God has destined for you to feel?*

I found myself answering her in exactly the same singsong tone which she herself had assumed:

> *I will not kiss the sword's cold steel,*
> *I would rather kiss Josepha.*

Since she was afraid that the sharp weapon might do me some serious injury, she was quite unable to make any sort of defensive gestures against me, and so it happened that I at last grasped her around her lovely waist and kissed her sulky, trembling lips most fervently.

Despite the awful sword of justice, whose blood-drenched blade rested between us, despite the foul prejudices of untold centuries which had marked this child as untouchable—I kissed with all my heart the ravishing daughter of the hangman.

CHAPTER FOURTEEN

ABOUT A WEEK AGO I had a note from a real-estate
man telling me that he had purchased a defunct hotel on the
upper West Side in New York and that, rummaging around in
the cellar of this derelict caravansary, he had come upon a suitcase containing three pair of socks, two pair of shorts, and about
twenty-seven boxes filled with letters and memoranda, most of
them bearing my name.

I quickly got in touch with this amiable man, and this morning
that treasure trove of mildewed memorabilia arrived in my study.
I must say I was quite moved when the musty odors of the past
literally rose into my nostrils, and as I fingered all those old letters
and memos addressed to an entity which had undergone such
radical alterations in the past two decades I couldn't help wondering whether I wasn't really trespassing on the privacy of an individual who had actually perished quite a while ago. Incidentally, a good many of these missives were postcards which I had

addressed to myself somewhere around 1948, and the messages I had scribbled were mostly reminders to phone certain people or to finish some work which I had promised to deliver on an exactly stipulated date.

Well, a good many of the characters referred to in those papers are now dead. A very few of them are still around, and, as far as I remember, they're still waiting for me to phone them. You see, I was living a pretty peripatetic existence during those fateful years and I hardly ever slept two successive nights in the same bed. Morphine was my constant and bitterly exacting mistress, and I really didn't have much time for a socially integrated life at all. Most of my waking hours were spent in devising means to obtain my poison, and as the years rolled on it became, naturally, more and more difficult for me just to keep going without also going completely under. That is how, in the days of my great down-and-outness, I came to leave behind me a whole flock of unpaid hotel bills and a great number of paper-laden suitcases.

It is strange how many people I have forgotten who were once very close to me, and it is even stranger how acute a memory I still have of some of them the moment my mind is accidentally jogged back into recalling them. In this dilapidated piece of luggage I found two letters which I had obviously been carrying about with me for nearly twenty years. The lady who had written these to me had once been known as Dr. Antoinette Kornikow.

Antoinette—or, better still, Toni—had been the mother-in-law of Yuzik Vanzler, a man who, for nearly a decade of my life, was about as close to me as anyone had ever been. He was married to Toni's daughter Edith, but, I'm sorry to say, we eventually had to give up our long and close friendship for a great variety of reasons, the most cogent of which was that Yuzik, activated by a relentless inner turmoil, coupled to a certain Muscovite intransigence, tried his best to alter the course of my whole existence. This situation had particularly depressing overtones for both of us, since we were always deeply and very sincerely devoted to one another. I cannot convey to you how greatly I came to miss him and how hard it was for me to forgo his biting sense of humor, his always candid observations on my often questionable behavior, and his obviously affectionate concern with the constantly fluctuating affairs of my existence. But the basic dichotomy between our totally dissimilar temperaments caused us to drift so far apart that finally I hardly ever saw him at all. *Requiescat in pace!*

Well, this mother-in-law of his, the aforementioned Antoinette Kornikow, had originally seemed to me just a bright-eyed, gray-haired practicing physician out of Boston somewhere, but, as soon as I got to know her a little better I discovered, with considerable surprise, that the real motivating purpose of her life was to be—an idealist.

You can't imagine how much I hate to use such a term in connection with someone whose memory I shall always cherish profoundly. I know perfectly well that nowadays one can't help feeling that such a word is bound to carry certain connotations of phoniness and, to a good many minds, it might even convey some implications of an acute psychopathological lesion.

Well, I suppose there isn't very much that I can do about it, since there can be no doubt that our vocabulary is slowly being corroded and disvalued—and this is particularly true about those words of high and exalted meaning which once carried the most treasured ethical, emotional and legal concepts of the human race. When we say "justice," or "honor," or "love," we have to surround these formerly significant sounds with five or six qualifying sentences just to establish a plausible platform on which their original authority can hope to survive without being stained by skeptical reservations.

So, Toni Kornikow was an idealist in the eighteenth- and part of the nineteenth-century sense of the word, and despite all of her startling modernity there was a certain air of old-fashioned truthfulness and purity in her manner, which I always found particularly beguiling. The Irish would have called her a dear *"old soul."*

She had come to the United States many years before in company with her husband, who was also a physician, and since they had fled out of Czarist Russia to escape the rigors of a notorious tyranny, they were naturally drawn to all causes that aimed at the eventual liberation of the downtrodden masses in their homeland. Like most Russian-born intellectuals in the early part of this century, Toni was, of course, a Socialist; and when the Bolshevik revolution proved successful she believed with unwavering certainty that at last reasonably civilized, if not millennial, conditions were about to come, rather belatedly, to the land of her birth.

When I first got to know her she was in her fifties and had acquired a large, lucrative medical practice in Boston. My acquaintance with her was brought about through her two grown children, Edith and Willy, who were, respectively, a trained nurse and a physician. As I have mentioned to you before, Edith in due time married my friend Yuzik Vanzler, whose ten-year involvement with me I have sketched with deliberate briefness since the wounds incurred in the course of that relationship are not so completely crusted over by indifference that I should care, even now, to make an overly minute examination of their badly healed scars.

At any rate, by the early twenties Toni had already been a divorcée for quite a number of years—but, as I have indicated, she had managed most admirably for herself and for her children —and in the early days of our acquaintance it was quite obvious that her humanitarian expectations could hardly reach higher pinnacles of optimism than they achieved during that eventful time.

Of course, Russia was still in a profoundly troubled state, but she felt that many signs pointed to an eventual amelioration of the most onerous conditions which obtained during those desperately critical years. It stands to reason that Toni was extremely anxious to visit the Old Country in order to see with her own eyes what alterations had been brought about by so epoch-making a revolution, and finally—in 1926, I believe—she managed to make the trip. She was absolutely bubbling over with anticipation when she boarded the boat in New York, and we could hardly wait for her to return, since we ourselves had been greatly keyed up by her infectious enthusiasm for this fantastically novel experiment in human affairs.

Well, she stopped by to visit with us after she came back, and although the reality had failed to live up to her expectations her optimism was certainly far from dimmed. She seemed to have suffered a few rather disheartening personal setbacks, but she had unlimited faith in the future, a future that was going to provide those potent anodynes which spring from memories of common suffering endured in the struggle for a common freedom.

I think I ought to apprise you, at this point, that Toni had for many years held birth-control seminars for the wives of working people up in Boston and that, in the course of these activities, she had, on a few occasions, managed to run afoul of some of the police authorities in that community. Toni once told us, with considerable amusement, that in each of her skirmishes with the law some rather aloof Back Bay ladies of definitely aristocratic lineage had invariably instructed their attorneys to pay her fines.

"I suppose they are really quite stuffy," she said, "but they are an independent lot and they just don't like people to be pushed around. I must say these old New Englanders seem to be the last repositories for that spirit of independence which once made this country great."

In any event, when Toni landed in Moscow she at once sought out the proper authorities where her knowledge and experience in the field of birth control might be most readily welcomed. Also, she had brought with her a special formula for a contraceptive paste, to which she owned the exclusive patent.

And this is where she first came up against that ultimately perfected form of buck-passing for which Russia and her various satellites have since become the world's most monstrous examples. Although abortions were being performed every hour on the hour, the clock around, by practically every doctor in the Soviet Union, and the medical profession was deeply alarmed for the general welfare of the adult female population, *nobody* wanted to be responsible for accepting Toni's desperately needed panacea. Her assistance was offered gratuitously, of course; nevertheless, she spent endless days antechambering a variety of clinical factotums; and even the properly authorized heads of all the national medical societies were unable to make any sort of definitive commitments. It was the tragicomic saga, symbolic of every monolithic state bureaucracy, in which no one actually had the right to initiate *anything* which had not first achieved the approval of the most powerful cabal inside the ruling presidium. The ruling presidium was up on Sinai issuing *ukases* just about as often as there were abortions being performed, but, unhappily, a good many of these stern directives which thundered down from the dialectical heights contradicted some equally hallowed commands which had been issued only a very short time before. So it was no wonder that it was practically impossible to find anyone inside the vast borders of Soviet Russia who was prepared to say "yes" or "no" to anything more potentially compromising than his readiness to accept a glass of tea. And even in this seemingly harmless area there were some overly timid ones who hesitated to give too ready an acquiescence to the tea proposition for fear it might be interpreted as an implied counterrevolutionary criticism of good plain Bolshevik water.

At any rate, poor Toni finally filed the chemical formula of her paste at some government office and consoled herself with the thought that revolutions are bound to be pretty upsetting to everybody who happens to get mixed up with them. After all, a revolution is not a picnic.

She also told us how, one day, she had applied for permission to attend a congress of Soviet philosophers and how, this permission having been speedily and graciously granted, she had placed herself in the front row of a balcony from which she had an unimpeded view of the large and beautifully decorated hall.

She still spoke Russian fluently, and since, in those comparatively early days of the Soviet regime, a good deal of freedom could still be exercised, at least in literary and purely intellectual circles, she found with pleasure that the discussions among these obviously very learned disputants were not often marred by dialectical distortions generally required to sustain the sacred Marxian bias.

However, she noticed after a while that whenever some important point was about to be scored or some particularly lucid conclusions had nearly been drawn by any of the distinguished-looking participants, one member at this gathering—a tall, very hairy individual by the name of Chetkoff—would spring into action and, by the persistent introduction of some highly splenetic irrelevancies, manage very effectively to disrupt the intellectual flow of these otherwise most orderly proceedings. When this had happened about ten or twelve times, the presiding chairman cleared his throat and directly addressed himself to this chronic interrupter. He said, "Would Comrade Chetkoff be good enough, for the sake of general clarification, to furnish this meeting with some identifying credentials and to let us know what particular school or authorized academic body he represents?"

"Aha!" said Chetkoff. "So you want to know who I am and whom I represent. Well, Comrade, I can tell you in six words who I am. I am a *consumer* of philosophy! That's who I am—and, what is more, I don't care two damaged kopecks for the stuff you are handing out here!"

And he forthwith sat down.

Later on, after Stalin came into power, Toni had a very bad time of it. She couldn't take Stalin even from the very beginning, and so she settled all her hopes on the exiled Trotsky; and, I daresay with her faith in him and his principles quite undiminished, she finally died.

One more note on Toni.

One day one of her patients, the childless wife of a doctor, came to consult her on what she intimated was a rather delicate and even somewhat peculiar matter.

"Come on," said Toni, "after all, I've read Krafft-Ebing and I'm not only a doctor, I'm also a woman. So don't be afraid; speak up."

"Well, Dr. Kornikow," said the patient, "as you know, I've

been married a little less than fifteen years. Frankly, I don't know quite how to tell you about this, but during all that time, whenever my husband and I had sexual relations, I never really felt anything. You know what I mean? I had mostly just a feeling of irritation. But then, just about a week ago—I don't know how it happened—I suddenly had—"

"A climax," suggested Toni.

"I suppose that's what it must have been," said the patient. "It was a feeling I've never had before in all my life, and it shook me up so I think I must have made some kind of a noise—a yelp, maybe, or something. At any rate, the minute I made that sound my husband threw a full glass of cold water into my face. He thought I was having a fit or something. And now, Dr. Kornikow, what do you think I should do?"

"You are still a very young woman," said Toni, "and I certainly think you should get yourself a divorce before that husband of yours gets a chance to drown you."

That was Toni.

Another letter in my wayworn suitcase was signed "Konrad." It was a note from my old friend Konrad Bercovici, whose sprightly conversation and wit had garnished a good many years of my life. We had known each other for almost four decades, and during all that time, in sickness or in health, in luxury or in the dumps, I could imagine only very few people whose companionship offered such constant and lively social dividends.

It was he who was largely responsible for my prolonged stay in Paris in 1928, and it was he, also, who made my sojourn there into the most delightful of experiences. He owned an apartment at that time at 24 rue de Verneuil, and I well recall one minor festival at his home which brought me some particularly unexpected amusement. When I say "minor," I mean that there were only about sixteen people gathered for some afternoon drinks and snacks and that the party lasted less than ten hours.

Well, at any rate, it was on this occasion that I met for the first time the distinguished American psychiatrist Dr. A. A. Brill and his friend and colleague, Dr. Menas Gregory. Dr. Gregory was, at that period of his career, head of the psychiatric department at Bellevue Hospital, and both he and Dr. Brill had come to Paris for a special psychiatric get-together of some kind, which was scheduled to begin the following week. Although the official business which had brought them to France was still in the offing, they indicated to us that they had already strained and, to some extent, even wearied themselves with a good many preliminary labors among their various multilingual confreres.

I'm trying to make clear to you that their afternoon's relaxation at Bercovici's was in the nature of an almost luxurious indulgence on their parts and that the voluble amiability which surrounded them was completely bereft of any immediate psycho-clinical overtones. As the day began to turn toward dusk and the spirit of general sociability rose perceptively higher, I noticed that the two visiting psychiatrists had withdrawn to the partial confines of an adjacent alcove, out of which a great deal of unrestrained laughter soon proceeded to emanate. Our host, who loved to share all the available joviality with every one of his guests, looked with mock disapproval on this private mardi gras and urged the two medicos to give the rest of us a chance to get in on their big yak, too.

"Come on," he said. "I have hardly ever known any psychiatrists who laughed out loud at anything anybody ever told them. Whatever you say to them is at once subject to deep analytical scrutiny and, although I've heard them give out with some pretty terribles jokes in my time, they never really find anything funny in what anyone else ever says."

"You do us a great injustice," said Dr. Brill. "I personally think that a good sense of humor is a basic requirement in the makeup of a competent psychiatrist. You know that I translated Freud into English, and I can tell you that the old man, who was sometimes rather desperately ill, nevertheless appreciated humor in all its forms and was never deficient in recognizing its highly prophylactic significance."

"There you go again," said Konrad. "The prophylactic significance of humor is the sure death of any joke. Just the same, I'm anxious to hear what the two of you had been cackling about when I interrupted you."

"Actually we weren't laughing at anything particularly funny," said Dr. Gregory. "In fact, it was more in the nature of an inter-office joke—or, rather, an interprofessional joke."

"Fine," said Konrad, "let's hear it."

"It has to do with a very young colleague of ours," said Dr. Gregory, "who, naturally enough, has to remain anonymous. Well, one day a man showed up at his office and said he'd been recommended by his medical man to find some psychiatric help and that is what he had come for. The medical man was a person vaguely known to the psychiatrist, and so he proceeded to question the patient about his problem. After a good deal of round-about talk, the stranger, whose name was Woodrow Warwick, said that he had an absolutely irrepressible urge to utter a lot of objectionable words out loud and that this often happened to him on occasions when it might prove really quite disastrous. Well, the psychiatrist had never treated such a case before, but, as a preliminary measure, he urged the patient to say anything that came into his mind during the next half hour and to see what would come of it. Sure enough, this Warwick person proceeded to say every possible dirty word that anyone could ever have imagined. When the half hour was over, he was, of course, a little embarrassed, but, at the same time, he seemed to be in much better emotional shape than when he had first arrived. And so, over the weeks, as these sessions proceeded and Warwick went on shouting his filthiest epithets at the doctor, the condition of the patient continued to show really marked improvement. One day the psychiatrist finally asked Warwick what it was that he did for a living.

" 'Oh, I'm in Wall Street,' said the patient. 'I'm a broker and I have some very great responsibilities. Handling a lot of money that belongs to other people is a very serious matter.'

" 'I'm sure it is,' said the doctor. 'Well, any time you hear of anything particularly good down there, let me know. I'd like to make an easy dollar once in a while, too.'

" 'Sure thing,' said Warwick, and once again he launched himself into his obscene gutter rigmarole.

"Well, about six weeks later he said, 'Doc, if you really want to take a whirl on the market, I think *now* is the time for you to try it.'

" 'Fine,' said the doctor. 'What do you advise me to do?'

"To make a long story short, Mr. Woodrow Warwick marched out of that office that same afternoon carrying a check for fifteen thousand dollars of the doctor's money in his coat pocket. What is more, our psychiatrist friend never saw hide nor hair of him again. And now comes the craziest part of it. You see, we've talked to several dozen psychiatrists in the last few days, and about seven of them have been rooked in the selfsame manner by the selfsame man."

"How come the police didn't catch up with him?" said Konrad.

"Ah, well, that is a rather ticklish matter when you really come to analyze it," said Dr. Gregory. "After all, a man in our profession is assumed to be something of a *Menschen-kenner*, a sort of superphrenologist who can spot what goes on with people the moment he lays eyes on them. Of course, this is just a popular misconception, and certainly it is complete nonsense; nevertheless, I can assure you that it couldn't possibly do any psychiatrist one bit of good to have it published abroad that he had been the gullible victim of a confidence man. His patients might not really care to receive psychiatric treatments from such a trusting dupe. At any rate, nobody anywhere reported anything to the police, and so Mr. Warwick just moved on to his next scientifically accredited victim. In short, we have come to the conclusion that this character specializes in bilking only psychiatrists and, what is more, he very thoughtfully equips all of them with a lush vocabulary of the most lurid and unseemly swearwords, which they can later employ whenever they think of him."

Apropos of meetings in France, my dear friend George Grosz once told me that he happened to be staying in Paris when a meeting of The Third International Writers' Congress was being held there. This literary conclave was, of course, just an excuse to launch the usual flood of Communist propaganda gibberish, and since George had already suffered his own bitter disillusionment with the whole Marxian setup he decided to remain most painstakingly clear of the whole shebang. He ran into a few of the delegates in the various coffeehouses around town, and, quite naturally, these ex-comrades of his either cut him completely dead or made some appropriately derogatory remarks about his cowardly defection.

At any rate, he was staying at the Hotel Conseil d'Etat, near the rue du Bac, and one evening when he returned home he found a young German writer, whom he recalled rather vaguely, sitting down in the diminutive lobby waiting for him.

"I was quite surprised to see this chap," said George, "because I had surely never exchanged even a single word with him. However, I noticed at once that he had lost quite a bit of weight since I had last seen him, and it appeared to me that he looked rather distraught, too. Well, I thought he'd probably run out of funds, and so I figured it was more than likely that he'd just come around to hit me up for a couple of hundred francs.

"I had already put my hand into my pocket when this fellow—he could have been no more than about twenty-two or twenty-three at the time—suddenly grabbed me by the arm and said, 'Dear Mr. Grosz, I beg you to save my sanity and my life! I know that you are a very warmhearted man, and that is the only reason why I've had the courage to wait here and make my appeal to you.'

"As he talked, his name came back to me and I recalled that he had published a few short poems of a rather sentimental nature in one of the magazines that I once used to work for. His name was Magnus Breitheim and, I must say, almost at once I felt rather unreasonably sorry for him.

" 'What is it, Mr. Breitheim?' I said. 'Are you short of money or something?'

" 'Not at all,' he said. 'I have more money than I need. Believe me, it is a matter of life or death for me or I would never have dared to come here to disturb you.'

" 'Let's go to my room,' I said. 'We'll be able to talk more quietly there.'

" 'Dear Mr. Grosz,' he said, 'it is not necessary to have a long talk at all. My whole tragedy can be told in half a dozen sentences.'

" 'All right,' I said, 'go ahead.'

" 'You see, Mr. Grosz, I left Germany two years ago and I have since become a permanent citizen of the Soviet Union.'

" 'Yes,' I said, 'I remember hearing something about that. And what has happened to you since?'

" 'Well, some six months ago an aunt of mine died, right here in Paris, and when her will was probated, it was discovered that she had left me all of her money. So I proceeded to apply for a permit to come to France in order to collect my legacy, but the authorities in Moscow decided that I should wait until the literary congress was scheduled to take place here, and then I could come along as one of the representative delegates.'

" 'And what seems to have gone wrong?' I said.

" 'What went wrong is that I, most unfortunately, committed a very rash act on my way to this country. You see, I was standing at a railroad station in Zurich, when I happened to notice a train that was about to go back to Germany late that afternoon. Well, that same evening, without meaning any harm, I sat down in my hotel room and wrote a sonnet to that train. You see, I'm a lyric poet, Mr. Grosz, and, as I looked at that little locomotive pulling those clattering coaches along the tracks which led back to my poor motherland, I couldn't resist addressing myself to that train—telling it to take my greetings to the dear fir trees, and to the brooks which bubbled along within sight of the road bed, and to the thin church steeples that stood in the quiet valleys along the way. It was just a harmless poem, really, but it was my misfortune that a Swiss friend of mine sent it to a magazine in Bern and that it was printed there, just ten days ago. And now I am, of course, in the most terrible trouble with all the members of the congress here, because certain delegates have accused me of publicizing reactionary sentiments which are bound to give aid and comfort to detrimental revisionist tendencies. They say I have acted as a Nazi apologist when, as a matter of fact, I left Germany especially on account of them, and the last thing I'd ever want to do is to appear as one of their defenders.'

" 'Tell me, Mr. Breitheim,' I said, 'did you write anything at all besides what you have just told me? Anything about politics, for instance?'

" 'Not one single word,' he said. 'But you can just imagine what a terrible dilemma I have landed in. Nobody wants to listen to me. I'm being ostracized by all the comrades, and I finally fell into such despair that I decided to come here and to ask for your help.'

" 'Well,' I said, 'you know that I myself am in very bad odor with the members of this congress, but, if you will give me a chance to think about your problem for a few days, it may be that I might arrive at some helpful suggestion for you. Just promise me one thing: you won't phone me and you won't come here until you hear from me. You see, at present I'm not exactly a man whose reputation is likely to do you the least bit of good. In fact, you are risking getting into an even worse mess if it becomes known that you asked for my assistance.'

"He promised, of course, and, after he had left me, I went over to the Deux Magots, where I knew that several of the top delegates sometimes used to get together for an occasional sausage spread and, while comparing notes on the latest state secrets, they would also down a goodly number of imported dark beers. I happened to be in luck that evening, for, sure enough, a couple of my pals from the Berlin days were sitting in a secluded corner, quietly impersonating Lenin and Trotsky. Of course, at first they were pretty hostile to me, but after a few moments, when they discovered why I had sought them out, they listened to me with a show of reasonable grace. Now one of these lads, whose name was Hellmuth Sonderling, had been pretty close to me in the old days, and it was he who, finally, agreed to take up the matter of the loused-up poet with The Responsible Committee on Back-sliders and Cosmopolitanism.

" 'I'll let you know about it at your hotel,' he said. 'I'll either phone you or send you a pneumatique.'

"I went home and I didn't hear anything further for the next couple of days, but on the third day Hellmuth did, finally, call me up.

" 'I think,' he said, 'that the matter you talked to me about will be arranged so that this foolish young man will not be damaged for life.'

" 'That's very kind of you, Hellmuth,' I said, 'and I'm certainly glad to hear that your group is not so hopelessly doctrinaire and hidebound after all. Tell me, how did they get around to excusing this breach of party etiquette or whatever the hell it was that he had been charged with?'

" 'You are very funny,' said Hellmuth. 'Just as funny as usual. Nevertheless, I see no reason for *not* telling you. It was decided, only this morning, that since Magnus Breitheim had expressed feelings of general recollective amity only toward the landscapes of his youth, and since he had uttered these emotions exclusively in rhyme, without any discernible propagandistic intentions, it will be the accepted policy of the committee from now on to consider that *nostalgia* in itself is *not necessarily* a *counterrevolutionary* symptom if it happens to be the work requirement of a properly certified lyric poet.' "

During the time when I abandoned hotel bills and suitcases all over the country, I certainly used to eat in some pretty strange places. By *strange* I only mean obvious; I ate in diners and coffee-pots where really unbelievable things go on "nourishment-wise," as some inspired advertising magician would say.

Around the big cities, like New York, Boston, Chicago, San Francisco, and even Hollywood, you can often get excellent food, particularly in the large cafeteria chains; you just have to appear there at the right time and not wait until the very life-blood has been steamed out of everything. However, in the smaller beaneries all over this land the grub is so utterly revolting that I just can't bear to think about it. Short-order cooking is almost always destined to be rather monstrous, since its basic momentum is propelled by lard, or bacon grease, or some of the other dreadful fatty substances which abound in the hellish places where it is practiced. The horrible crap that is dished out in these awful joints is certainly a stain, *an irremovable grease stain,* on the gastronomical escutcheon of the United States.

But then, in the winter of '48, I suddenly got an idea for a musical, and one of the numbers in this junk-inspired opus of mine was supposed to be a song-and-dance interlude called "The Ballad of the Coffeepot." As far as I recall, I wanted to convey the passing hours of the days as they would come to affect life in such a beanery, and, in 1951, my talented friend Dick Freitas even wrote a fine melodic score for that whole show. At any rate, I just rediscovered the original first draft of this particular lyric, in that selfsame prodigal suitcase which just recently turned up at my house.

THE BALLAD OF THE COFFEEPOT

The roadside diner and the Coffeepot,
The hamburger stand at the railroad station,
This is the melting pot of the nation,
This is what no other country has got.
This is the melting pot of the nation.

French-fried potatoes, mountain-high,
Scoops of vanilla, apple pie,
Coffee and cake, both raisin and plain,
The syndicated sandwich wrapped in cellophane.
The fruits of the land for the many, not the few,
Sweating in a steam bath while waiting for you.

To the smell of coffee and frying ham,
The flies wash their faces on a pile of Spam.

The bleary chorine in a cloud of Chanel,
In a blouse that is more than revealing,
Has plumped herself down with her morning Coke,
And studies herself while she's blowing smoke.
The cop on the beat grabs a quick, free snack.
The day has started out on its shining track.

Twelve o'clock noon at the Greasy Spoon,
Near Boston Common, off Hollywood and Vine,
The milling millions stand up to dine.
Mountains of beef, and oceans of java,
Lakes of lard like bubbling lava,
Rivers of orangeade and pies,
The sizzling fat blots the sun from the skies.
Here is the world's truly best fed nation,
Taking out some minutes for its noonday ration.
Here is the well-filled, noisy mob,
Ready to go back to the afternoon's job.

At four o'clock, when the English take their teas,
High-school minors, in a hundred thousand diners,
Lap up apple pie and cheese.
Nations may patronize our gastric condition,
But hardly a minor, in our primitive diner,
Has ever come down with malnutrition.

Ham and lamb on the evening breeze,
Lovers holding hands while their home fries freeze;
Kids eating franks, cutting teen-age capers,
Lonely men with their evening papers.
Hamburgers, ice cream, tomatoes and beer;
Never mind what day it is, what month, what year,
The habits of a nation are provided, here.

Twelve at night, some customers are tight,
Tomorrow's news just hot off the press;

Two swells sipping coffee, in evening dress.
Against one wall, two homeless vagrants
Add their aroma to the Coffeepot fragrance.
The cop on the beat looks in from the street,
The forces of life are blowing retreat.
Only one skillet still simmers at large,
The odors of the washroom have taken charge.

At two at night, the tiles shine bright,
The place is quiet, the streets are still,
The counterman is sitting behind the till;
He's drinking his coffee and munching a bun,
You can tell that his face never sees the sun.
The coffee urn shines, the stove is clean,
The flies are asleep on the window screen.
Just one lonely couple, come late from a dance,
Still sit in a corner, like two in a trance.
They stare at each other and smile and sigh,
While the stillness of night goes tiptoeing by.

CHAPTER FIFTEEN

M OST MORNINGS, before I begin my work, I usually read a couple of newspapers, and by the printed evidence of those dismal sheets we are certainly in a pretty terrible shape. I don't mean just according to the news reports either. I find the cultural notes and sidelights on our civilization very often even more depressing than the columns devoted to the state of international tensions and the ones given over to general world disasters.

At any rate, last Monday morning I suddenly decided to clean up the corner of my room in which I always do my writing, and among the vast accumulation of papers that I eventually had to examine I came across a number of rather rancorous doodlings—which I now submit for your inspection in the following pages.

Each of these scribbles was quickly executed, and every single one of them represents an immediate response to some potent irritant at the very moment when it happened to impinge upon me most poignantly.

My only regret is that some of the very best among them are really quite unprintable.

BLUT UND EHRE
(*Blood and Honor*)

They have revived *die Mensur* at a number of German universities.

This means that the post-Hitlerite youth is dueling once more. Dueling with sharp sabers.

Remember? In the old days, under Kaiser Wilhelm, they used to scar each other up, too.

The news commentator who announced this revival of carefully codified brutality said that a great many influential German *alte Herren* are more inclined to give jobs to young men who display some visible testimony to their masculine virility.

In short, those gruesome old sons of bitches have not yet smelled enough blood in their lifetimes. They're eagerly restaging all their dehumanizing activities from the fencing abattoirs of their past.

They always begin by spilling the gore of their own youngsters before they are finally ready to inundate the whole world again.

I'll show you what a really curious codger I have finally become: you see, I am not one bit less frightened of those *alte Herren* in Germany than I am of the dear comrades, Khrushchev and Mao Tse-tung, waiting for us a little farther over to the east.

THE SCIENTIST

This bovine individual could have been a reasonably satisfactory night watchman, in a neighborhood where there wasn't too much going on.

But he had an uncle who once made a neat fortune in the doctoring business, so his family chipped in and he somehow managed to worm his way toward a medical degree.

Now he is a sacred cow in whom the milk of human kindness curdled quite a few years ago.

This arrogant dunderhead is constantly blowing off about the glorious role of the American Medical Association. He pretends to believe that it is a totally disinterested body of men, dedicated to the highest principles of medical research and scientific progress.

If you dare to hint that it is just a crass pressure group devoted almost exclusively to the financial advantages to be gained by its membership, he will, of course, call you a Communist.

So it inevitably follows that the basic axiom of his life is that anything that doesn't put money into his pockets is *Socialized Medicine*.

DIAGNOSTICS ON THE DARK CONTINENT

This creature knows Africa like he knows his own armpits.
I can assure you that there is more light in those hairy hollows
than in any of his most lucid dissertations on his all-time
favorite subject.
He insists on leaning backward to give everyone his just due.
However, he is convinced that those childishly vain, congenitally
dishonest dark people will take at least half a millennium
to come up to certain basic standards.
His standards, I suppose.

THE CONDITIONED REFLEX

These little men from the Radical Right have been chronically
   constipated since earliest infancy.
This curious condition is entirely due to the fact that they never
   could accustom themselves to the idea that there were
   some things in the world which they just *had* to give up.
They don't even suspect that most of their ideas, and nearly all of
   their cherished aspirations, are predicated on the deplorable condition of their poor, tormented sphincters.

THE MORAL ARBITERS

It must be obvious to the meanest intelligence that this is a girl with talent. Her love affairs, marriages and divorces are consuming more space in the tabloids than almost any other subject currently agitating the attention of an apprehensive world.

When she finally takes her overdose of sleeping pills, the editorial cockroaches who are largely responsible for her lurid reputation will write moral homilies about sticking it out with the good life, behind the family washing machine.*

---

* This piece was written in the middle of July 1962. I had the subject photostated at the firm of Joseph Merritt in Hartford, Connecticut, one week before Marilyn Monroe's death. I'm not implying that I foresaw her sad end; all I'm telling you is that I was describing a generic type facing up to a pretty standard state of affairs. As far as I'm concerned, the situation is permanently standard and the type is still wildly at large. I knew Marilyn Monroe as a highly sensitive, sadly troubled human being and I was deeply shocked when I heard of her end. No one could have foreseen this sad denouement, and I greatly deplore it.

A MODERN PHENOMENON

This is a Teen-age Ideal.
It is a millionaire.
They say it sings.

THE BLEEDING HEART

This little lady is active in Charity.

In case you don't know what this implies, it simply means that she
never gives *anybody anything*.

Since her life is dedicated to large-scale kindnesses and she spends
all of her time measuring destiny for some cast-off
clothing, she enjoys a semiofficial status which permanently exempts her from every form of personal kindness.

Extracurricularly she also acts as a feed-line for certain notori-
ously inaccurate society columnists, who compensate
her for these labors by occasionally featuring her name
in some of their dismal reports.

Most recently, she has achieved some measure of additional popularity because she can always be counted upon to render a few particularly scandalous anecdotes about the
intimate lives of the Kennedys.

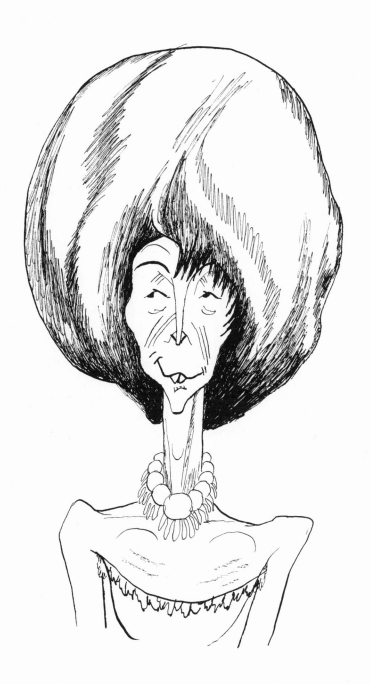

THE GUARDIAN OF OUR RIGHTS

This dreadful loudmouth is always talking about "Freedom!"

He has a rather unique version of this commodity in mind, and what is more, this special product of his always bears his own peculiar trademark.

He is in politics, of course, which means that you and I have been supporting him and his nepotistically dependent leeches throughout most of their adult lives.

It goes without saying that he has always had the benefit of totally unpaid medical care, and the one thing that worries him constantly is the creeping socialism which is slowly beginning to invade every aspect of our modern existence.

Also, I don't want you to be fooled by the fact that on some dark night, a whimsical gene, in an unusually playful moment, happened to hang a scrotum on this monster, because this has never yet interfered with his capacity to play the role of a very successful prostitute.

THE PERIPATETIC LIGHTHOUSE

As a teen-ager he was something of a religious fanatic, and, in-
    deed, for a while it seemed as if he might even come to
    study for the priesthood.
Later on he joined the Communist movement, and after a widely
    heralded public recantation, he finally threw in his lot
    with the extremest political rightists.
I'm sure he must be a proud asset to any cause that can enlist his
    allegiance.
While it lasts.

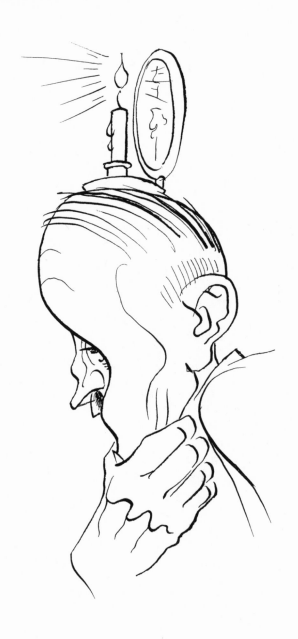

THE ORACLE

This pseudo-feminine disaster does beauty commercials on the
  TV screen.

She is constantly talking about skimpy eyelashes, shaggy eyebrows, skin eruptions, elbow roughness, droopy curls,
  hair odors, underarm discomforts and crotch insecuri-
  ties.

Every time she speaks about these personal blemishes I can't help
  associating these calamities with her own particular person.

In fact, as she continues yammering away at me, she seems to be
  getting uglier and uglier by the minute.

Somebody once told me that she earns around a quarter of a million dollars a year.

If that is true, I think she is shamefully underpaid.

THE FETISHES

I have never been to any kind of a good-sized party, either in
New York or in Hollywood, without running into
these two revolting creatures.
They bring to these celebrations neither wit nor humor nor
charm, and yet everybody goes right on inviting them.
Why?
I think they serve a good, constructive purpose, because no first-
class party can ever function properly without at least
a couple of fourteen-carat freaks.
You see, I have figured out that most of the people at such gatherings meet without joy and suffer long hours of almost
unrelieved boredom together.
So, it seems inevitable to me that sooner or later the victims of
such gregarious compulsions would be bound to come
to blows unless a diversion were provided, by means of
which all of the pent-up communal loathing could
spend itself in some comparatively harmless manner.
In short, these two flagrant disasters actually serve as social lightning rods for the concentrated nausea which hangs like
a dense cloud over most of these festive gatherings.

SNAPSHOT OF A HERO

This little man earns sixty-seven dollars a week, and he and his
   wife and their seven children live in one room on upper
   Park Avenue in New York City.
The civically high-minded group which, during each yuletide
   season, raises decoratively illuminated fir trees along that
   particular street, plants them only where the most fashionable dog-walkers are in residence.
Beyond Ninety-sixth Street, where children manifest themselves
   in the greatest possible abundance, nobody has ever
   bothered to put up any Christmas trees.
At any rate, this constantly defrauded and everlastingly harassed
   creature has a namesake who earns vast fortunes every
   afternoon at the *corrida*.
You see, his name happens to be Antonio Ordóñez too, but, unfortunately, there isn't any sort of glamor connected
   with him, since he is obviously condemned to spend all
   the rest of his life as just a small-time billfighter.

THE LADY INTERVIEWER

She is a chronic freeloader from way back. When she finally arrives at your home, one hour behind the specified time, she makes eight phone calls, in the course of which she smokes up at least half a pack of your favorite *Gaulois*.

She doesn't just drop names, she bounces them off you like underdone dumplings, and, although you know that she has been intimate with the leading statesmen of the whole wide world, you finally can't resist the suspicion that her truly closest friends, the ones she feels most relaxed with, have all appeared on eleven of the twelve preceding pages.

She doesn't know the Puerto Rican Antonio Ordóñez, and if she did, she'd only tell him he's damned lucky to *be* here.

CHAPTER SIXTEEN

THREE OTHER ITEMS in my beat-up suitcase held my attention for an entire evening last week, and the first of these was a letter written to me by Ronald Stockwell, a retired cotton broker, who was married to someone I had known for a great number of years.

Attached to this letter was a piece of paper containing some lines which I had obviously typed after receiving it.

This is what was written on the clipping:

"A well-known parasite, belonging to the Crustacea—the class of shrimps, crabs, lobsters, and crayfish—is *Sacculina*. The young *Sacculina* is an active, free-swimming larva much like the young prawn or young crab. But the adult bears absolutely no resemblance to such a typical crustacean as a crayfish or crab. The *Sacculina*, after a short period of independent existence, attaches itself to the abdomen of a crab and there completes its development while living as a parasite. In its adult condition it is simply a great, tumorlike sac bearing many delicate, rootlike suckers which penetrate the body of the crab host and absorb nutriment. The *Sacculina* has no eyes, no mouth parts, no legs or other appendages, and hardly any of the usual organs except reproductive organs."

I had copied this excerpt out of a book I had been reading in 1948, a book called *Parasitism and Degeneration*, by David Starr Jordan and Vernon Lyman Kellogg. It is a scientific work of great fascination, in which the changes in the structural conditions of certain parasites are most minutely recorded and brilliantly accounted for.

I remember that I typed that paragraph and attached it to Ronald's lettter with some notion that I might, at some time in the future, get around to doing a whimsical exegesis on the contents of that epistle with special elucidative reflections on the parasitic elements it contained.

Actually, there was nothing of the parasite about Ronald at all; quite the contrary, he had, as a matter of fact, throughout a good part of his life, merely acted out the role of the host crab. It was his wife, Cora Winton Stockwell, who would have served as the critical figure in my dissertation.

I had known Cora ever since she'd run away from a reasonably fashionable finishing school to get married to Sage Winters. Sage was only twenty at the time, and when his rich family heard about the elopement they instantly disowned him.

I suppose he must have had a few thousand dollars of his own when they ran off to Paris, because when I met them at the Café Dôme they were just like a couple of carefree kittens in a box full of fresh sawdust. They played being poor for about three months up near the Place du Tertre somewhere, but when it became obvious that his folks weren't going to relent in any foreseeable fashion, Sage went back to America in order to reason with them.

Nothing came of this excepting a substantial cash settlement for Cora, who next threw in her lot with a German boy called

Anton Heckert. His people had a lot of brewery money, and since he also showed rather a strong inclination to marry her, Cora eventually got paid off in marks.

In 1932 she came back to the States and set up an intellectual salon. On the walls of her house were Van Dongens, Masereels, and Fauconniers, most of them affectionately inscribed and none of them particularly good examples of these artists' labors.

Cora was in her prime then, and if you were anywhere between sixteen and twenty, or between fifty-eight and ninety-four, she would be exactly your type. She was dark and vivacious and she certainly had bulging, thyroid eyes. I think that her legs and ankles were her best features, and with the very young and the almost impotent, this is often a basic form of fetishism.

She generally entertained Thursday evenings, during the winter and early spring, and a good many of her callers were Ivy League undergraduates, who sat on the floor and talked a great deal about T. S. Eliot and Ezra Pound.

In 1934 she became engaged to Clem Horton, whose father was in big-time real estate, and before that relationship was finally severed, she wound up with a town house on East Sixty-fourth Street.

And then at last in 1940 she married again, and this time it was Ronald Stockwell, who was thirty years older than she and who set her up in a vast mansion in fashionable Westchester.

They entertained quite a bit, and after a while I even fancied that Cora was really quite fond of Ronald. He was tubby and bald, but a certain real sort of goodness radiated off that polished dome of his and I could imagine that someone like Cora, who had been around for quite a while, would be happy to settle down in the steady, protective shadow of Stockwell's obviously affectionate concern.

Well, as far as I was able to determine, she played it straight for about three and a half years, and then, one day when I ran into her at the Plaza she looked rather distraught and, what was much more serious, she seemed to have aged quite a bit.

"He's a very difficult man, really," she said. "You see, I'd heard that before we married he'd been playing the field pretty freely, but I can assure you that the worst kind of prude is a reformed rake. He never goes anywhere without me, and I might as well be living in the seraglio of the Grand Panjandrum. He even employs eunuchs, if you come right down to it. Those servants of his—all of them old retainers, it seems to me—are forever popping up where you least expect them, and the feeling I get is as if I were under constant, twenty-four-hour surveillance. You know, I wanted to learn how to fly, so Ronnie talked me into letting him get me a helicopter. Do you know why? So I could land on our front lawn and never even have to go out to the airport. The flying instructor was a friend of his, and he spent all his spare time talking to me about his six marvelous children and his absolute jewel of a wife. I just think I'm going to lose my mind."

"Why don't you travel with him?" I said.

"Oh, God! We went to Mexico last year, and we landed on a three-thousand-acre hacienda belonging to another pal of his—and it was like being in Alcatraz, with palm trees."

"Do you want to divorce him?" I asked.

"Of course not. When we first got married he invested all of my money for me, and after all these years I'm really completely dependent on him. I don't know where *I* begin and where *he* leaves off. I'm afraid I've been terribly stupid. I've managed things very badly."

"What are you doing in town?" I said.

"Oh, I've finally talked him into letting me take some courses at the New School. I'm taking some social science studies, and every so often I cut a few classes and float about town for a few hours on my own. Oh, here's my teacher—the short, dark man in the doorway. Would you be an angel and wave to him?"

I waved, of course, and I again thought of how many women nowadays are busy taking a variety of college extension courses merely because these educational activities represent an outlet for a general ovarian unrest.

At any rate, the newcomer, whose name was Morton Thrale, couldn't possibly have been more ill at ease than he was in Cora's hysterically chattering presence, and I assure you it was only out of a certain sympathy for his condition that I told them about something that had happened to me the week before. I just hoped that by directing the conversation into somewhat more general channels this Thrale person would get caught up in the drift of my yarn so that his cigarette would finally relax for a moment from its embarrassingly spastic gyrations.

"I've been on the Cape for about ten days," I said, "and I met a really odd New England character in a place called Plaidford. His name, believe it or not, was Vernal Snow, and he told me that for some thirty-five years he'd been general supervisor of a large estate in that neighborhood. At any rate, we talked quite a lot, and one day he asked me if I'd ever heard anything about the American heath hen. Of course, I never had.

" 'Funny thing about that bird,' he said. 'You know, for nearly a quarter of a century it has been believed to be absolutely extinct. There used to be great flocks of them in the past, but the farmers and the rest of the people around here just murdered them off by the thousands, and by the time the conservationists got into the picture they had all disappeared. Well, early one morning, about six-thirty or so, I happened to be walking on the outskirts of a small wood when I heard a completely unfamiliar sound. I tiptoed closer, and there in a small clearing, among the trees, was a bird I had never seen. What's more, this bird was doing some kind of a dance—a courting dance, it seemed to me—and, sure enough, it suddenly lowered one of its wings and started to beat the ground with it. It rolled its eyes, strutted about in a circle, and, every thirty seconds or so, it beat the ground with its wing. I couldn't have been more surprised. You see, about a year before I happened to read up some about the birds of New England and I'd read a description of just such a dance being done by the extinct heath hen. Well, you can imagine how excited I was. I kept absolutely still, and for nearly a whole hour that bird kept on whirling and banging away and nothing whatever happened. I tell you, I went back there every single day for the next two weeks, and every morning, there it was, carrying on as if its very life depended on it. Of course, it finally came to my mind that this bird that I was watching was the last survivor of a dying species and that he was just beating his brains out without, maybe, any chance in the world that another heath hen was still alive to hear him. And then one morning when I came out, he looked prety seedy to me. He looked almost as if he were molting. He had red rims around his eyes, and he only tapped the ground a couple of times. He cocked his head in all directions—listening with all his might, it seemed to me—and finally he gave a funny kind of hoarse cry and took off. And that's the very last I ever seen of him.' "

That was Mr. Snow's story as I told it, and I must say it diverted the economics teacher so much that he at last ordered a cocktail and settled quietly back to await its arrival with a socially suitable grin draped across his features.

After that meeting at the Plaza I lost sight of Cora for a while, and the next time I heard about her was from a friend, who told me that Ronald had instituted divorce proceedings against her.

Now then, during one of my visits to the Stockwell home up at Westchester, I had forgotten a book that I rather cherished; it was called *Chronicles of the Crusades* and had been written by a fascinatingly robust monk called Winsoufer (which means wine-bibber), a man who, according to his own reports, had actually been present in the Holy Land during one of the crusades. I hadn't been able to locate a duplicate copy of it anywhere, so I wrote a rather tactfully worded note to Ronald, asking him whether it was possible for him to locate my missing volume and would he please forward it to me.

His answer, written in longhand, was the letter which has now turned up again in my long-lost suitcase. I'll quote what he said verbatim:

DEAR ALEXANDER:

It was most pleasant to hear from you once more, and I hasten to reassure you about your book. It has gone off to you under separate cover this morning, and you will certainly receive it before the end of the week.

I know, of course, why you addressed yourself to me—since you probably believe that Cora and I are no longer together. This is, most happily, not the case at all. I daresay you heard that some time ago there was a certain misunderstanding between us. This is true enough. However, after we had been separated for nearly ten weeks a meeting was arranged between us by some mutual friends, and as the result of that meeting all our differences have simply evaporated.

Because you are such an old and close friend of Cora's, I will, under the seal of friendship, tell you what transpired at that meeting. When I first spoke to her after that ten-week separation, there was a definite feeling of strangeness between us, which I never would have believed possible.

You are an artist, and so you have a great deal of imagination, and I will not bother to explain in detail the nature of our disagreement. In fact, I had agreed to come to see Cora more to give a final goodbye than anything else. And then when we shook hands for the last time, she looked at me and said, "I want to tell you something that happened to me only last week. You see, I was up on the Cape, and there I met an old gamekeeper who told me the following story:

"He told me that it has for many years been known that the American heath hen has been totally extinct. But then one morning, he heard a strange sound in the woods, and when he crawled through the underbrush he saw a bird doing a love dance. It beat one wing on the ground and rolled its eyes, and he suddenly realized that he was watching the extinct heath hen. By some miracle, this last female had somehow survived, and she was looking and praying for her mate. Well, she did this dance for a whole week and finally disappeared."

And Cora said to me: "I'm just like that poor bird, too, Ronnie. I'm walking in circles in search of my mate, but nobody hears me and nobody minds my despairing call."

After Cora said that, my eyes were full of tears, and you will not be surprised that all is well between us. Better than ever before.

I have not shown Cora your letter. I want you to write to her separately and please come to see us again as you used to do in the old days.

And, please, if anyone hints to you that all is not well between us, then you can put them straight. The story is for your benefit alone.

My warmest regards,

RONALD STOCKWELL

I suppose the moral of this tale is that a successful parasite must stick to its host.

After Ronald died, Cora did manage to come into her own at last. Unfortunately, by that time, she too, like her scientific prototype, the *Sacculina*, had become just an old, shapeless bag.

Another exhibit out of that collection of written material which I had abandoned fourteen years ago is a letter written in my hand, and it is addressed "To my fifteen-year-old daughter, Alexandra."

Of course, almost everybody knows by now that I have no such daughter. Indeed, the fact that I *don't* has been quite a hang-up for me, since I'd always hoped, throughout the years, that I'd someday be lucky enough to become the father of one. As things stand, right at this moment, I haven't even managed to achieve a granddaughter of any kind; nevertheless, I have often so intensely and so persistently *imagined* such a desirable state of affairs that in the end I even seem to have written my nonexistent daughter a good-sized letter.

Here it is:

DEAR SANDY,

So you are in love, my darling; well, I can't tell you how happy this makes me. I have been in love several times in my life, and I can assure you that this has wonderfully enriched me in many, many ways. For instance, it has always quite miraculously sharpened my perceptions: the grass was greener, the dandelions were yellower, and the night air was sweeter and softer than I had ever known it to be. I think that to fall in love is the utmost in joy that this world has to offer. In your case there are certain obvious problems, since you are only fifteen years old and Karl is just barely eighteen.

All this would be of no consideration if we were Trobriand Islanders, but we are Americans living in New York City, and the year is 1948.

To tell you the truth, I have no conventional fatherly resources to draw upon, because I can see nothing basically wrong in the desire of young people to mate whenever sexual ripeness happens to come upon them. The difficulties which threaten such a course in our society have nothing to do with me, or how I feel. For better or worse, we are part of a scheme of life in which certain systems of order prevail, and these systems have been established by more or less common consent, so that the supposedly greatest good will accrue to the greatest possible number of ordinary people.

When I say "ordinary," I don't mean it in a derogatory sense at all. I just mean human beings who are destined to be neither geniuses nor saints. It goes without saying that saints are such high exemplars to the mass of mankind that we can leave them out of our reckoning altogether, while geniuses, who often violate the rules of established society, certainly come to suffer for these deviations in various cruel ways but they are, at least, sustained in their travails by the glory of their brilliant accomplishments.

The rest of us have only one choice left—and I will tell you about that in just a little while.

You see, Sandy, my love, Nature, the great mother of us all, seems to be constantly aiming for the highest goals. Never doubt that.

She gave the ugly, mud-wallowing lizard wings, and he turned into a soaring bird. She turned the hirsute, frightened caveman eventually into Isaiah, Euripides, Dante, Goethe, Shakespeare, and Thomas Jefferson. I think there is no boundary to the ambitions she may still have for us, and that is also the reason why she is so unbelievably wasteful. She turns us out by the uncountable billions for the sake of those rare spirits who come to matter so much in the sporadic illumination of mankind. I believe with all my heart that these comparatively very few are the only ones who bear any resemblance to the incalculable perfection which still lies slumbering in the womb of time.

At any rate, in her frightening prodigality she just wants us all to go on having babies, babies, babies—and since numbers, in our terms, have no meaning for her at all, her fructifying frenzy is truly without limits.

But then, at some lost point in time, man, the thinking animal, decided to take a hand in this whole business. Because of Nature's overpowering drive toward limitless proliferation, he found it useful to establish certain codes that gave more meaning to his day-by-day life, and all the teeming millions on this earth learned to evaluate their own entities in a reasonably just and equitable relationship with others. Out of these highly selective social patterns, they eventually came to garner rich harvests of consolations and rewards, which we have always associated with the orderly processes called—Civilization.

Hence, we have given up casting our seeds upon the wind like thistles and, largely because of those greater ones among us—the ones who made laws and set up beneficial statutes, and also those others who wrote psalms and poems which have done so much to ennoble human existence—we no longer copulate like a lot of compulsive goats on the open hillside.

So, you see, quite deliberately (very noble in aim, if not altogether in achievement), man proceeded to interfere with all this blind spawning and to devise certain rules and to set socially beneficial limitations to the endless procreative spasms which seem to animate all living things.

He decided to become responsible for himself and for those others who are destined to live alongside of him.

So, although we may not be able, by a mere effort of will, to achieve either genius or sainthood, we can, all of us, still aspire to become—heroes.

I tell you, Sandy, that anyone can become a hero in the truest sense of that word—a hero in the onward march toward a really meaningful civilization. It only requires that you be prepared to face the difficult problems of your human condition with a clear mind and a stout heart.

And now, my dearest, let us come back to your own specific situation.

You are in love, which is a great wonder and a supreme happiness, but if your love attempts to fulfill itself completely at this particular time, you are indeed more than likely to become pregnant.

If you should give birth to a child at this very early age, chances are that you will irremediably come to do serious damage to the sweet legend which might have been your life.

Karl, who is equally unprepared for the responsibilities of matrimony, is also certain to suffer untellable harm in the tenor and the tempo of his own development.

In short, I think it would be a most deplorable happening and would be certain to bring great sorrow to anyone who was concerned with your welfare.

So, in my final summation, what can I possibly say to you?

I can tell you to hold your head high in the joy and pride of your love. I want you to think of your life as a rich but unrenewable treasure, which only fools are ready to scatter impulsively, like so many unthinking yokels who dissipate their inheritance over a dart board at a county fair.

Above all else, my dearest, I wish you great good luck and, with a very full heart, I give you the assurance of my most steadfast devotion, no matter what may betide.

ALEX

The last number in my suitcase repertoire is a telegram which George Balanchine sent to me sometime in the mid-forties.

This dear friend was choreographing a musical play up in Boston at that time, and since the book of the show was rather weak, he had suggested my name for possible collaboration in the doctoring of this ailing script.

The telegram said: YOU WILL GET FIFTEEN HUNDRED DOLLARS RIGHT AWAY AND A SMALL PERCENTAGE OF THE GROSS.

So naturally I flew up to Boston and instantly entered into Bedlam on highly favorable terms. The show was in desperate shape, chiefly because the male star, who was a foreigner and had considerable difficulty with the English language, was categorically opposed to learning any new words. He knew all the old ones, which were mostly bad, but as long as he had already managed to memorize them, he simply refused to give them up. So much for him.

By the way, the name of this theatrical disaster was *Mr. Strauss Goes to Boston*, and it purported to be a re-creation of the actual events when Johann Strauss, the Waltz King, had visited that metropolis in the latter part of the last century.

I don't intend to torture you with the inanities of that confused plot. I just want to tell you that, since vast sums had already been expended on it, everyone connected with that lulu was just a walking nervous breakdown. Everyone, excepting George Balanchine, of course. He is a wonderfully even-tempered man, and, besides that, he knows his business thoroughly and, as a first-class choreographer, he was quite well aware that he personally had nothing whatever to worry about.

My role, of course, was quite different. As I've already indicated, I was having trouble with the cast, and since we only had a few days left before the opening in New York, I was hardly able to get any sleep at all.

Incidentally, the real story of Strauss's visit is so grotesque and unbelievable that it was practically impossible to invent anything more foolish or silly than what had actually taken place. It seems that twenty thousand singers had been assembled on Boston Common for that occasion, and when the Waltz King was ready to give the downbeat, a full-sized cannon had to be shot off to notify the participants who were involved in this shindig. I'm not inventing any of this stuff; I just read all about it in some of the old Boston newspapers, and I can tell you that those ancient clippings only managed to confuse and dishearten me still further. Also when that howitzer finally did go off, Maestro Strauss fell right off the podium and landed in one of the kettledrums. In fact, he had to have first aid before the concert could proceed.

We had other troubles, too.

In the hotel where the cast had been quartered they had two huge conventions going on at the same time. One was a gathering from a fraternal lodge of some sort, and the other one was a drunken spree sponsored by a vast national sales organization.

You can just imagine what went on there.

And then, again, maybe you *can't*, either.

You see, we had fourteen chorus girls in that show, and they simply couldn't pass through that damned hotel lobby without getting absolutely goosed into a state of galloping hysterics. Those simian celebrants, in their permanently boozed-up condition, were loaded with electric teasers and automatic hotfoots of all kinds, and the most harmless thing they did was just to blow sneezing powder all over everybody's hair.

And even this wasn't quite as harmless as it sounds. One evening one of those middle-aged fauns blew a big blast of this itchy powder at one of our feathered dancers, and later on, when, in the course of her performance, she did her usual fifteen pirouettes, that crazy stuff was dislodged out of her curls and it naturally flew all over that damned stage. In something less than one minute a dozen or so people were sneezing their fool heads off in full view of the audience, and we certainly got a great big laugh we hadn't planned on. I was in such despair about that show that, for a moment or so, I even considered peppering everything with sneezing powder, just to liven things up a bit.

In the meanwhile, we had a daily crisis convoying those poor broads to the theater every morning. At last, by the merest accident, I finally hit upon a workable solution.

You see, as I was wandering around that hotel one day, just shortly before dawn, I discovered that there was a laundry chute leading from the mezzanine floor straight down into the boiler room. When I asked one of the bellhops about this, he told me that he, and most of the boys working around that section, would often slide down into the basement along that very route.

Well, that was our way *out*. The way *in* was never really much bother, because the whole cast generally went on rehearsing after every night's performance and by the time we got back to the hotel it was always so late that most of the dizzy celebrants were far too drunk to give us any sustained difficulties.

To tell you the truth, I was greatly surprised that Boston had become such a popular gathering place for conventions. I remember that when I first came to this country, Chicago used to be the great Mecca for all of these fraternally sponsored binges. When

I lived out there for a short period, I even got a badge of some kind from one of the room clerks in my hotel, because I seemed to be the only one in the whole damned town who wasn't wearing an identification tag of any sort. I felt positively naked. Well, after I'd hung that metal pastry on my lapel, everybody in town gave me a friendly smile, and I even came in for a lot of the free sandwiches and soft drinks that the ladies' auxiliaries were dishing out all over the place.

But back to Boston.

As I've already mentioned to you, when we started to drop our ladies-of-the-ensemble into the laundry chute, our troubles, on that score at least, were over. We always had about three cabs waiting for them out in a nearby alley, so nobody got mauled or suffered any more electric-shock treatments and those blithering old goats just had to find some other helpless victims on whom to practice their behind-the-barn type of playfulness.

So far, so good.

And then one morning, while I was standing guard near some heavily loaded linen baskets which acted as shock absorbers for our gravitationally propelled cast members, and just as the first ones started to fly through the air in a flurry of frothing petticoats, I noticed with horror that one of the worst of those convention-eering nuisances was watching this animated scene in salivating enchantment, while leaning up against the banister of the staircase which led down into this subterranean refuge.

I was so shattered by the sight of that monster that, like a great many people when faced by an overwhelming crisis, I did absolutely nothing. I just hustled the girls quickly out of the door and realized with a thundering heart that the jig was up.

The following day, when I went down to reconnoiter, I had another surprise coming: the joint was quiet and there wasn't anybody around at all. So, with all my fingers and all my toes crossed, and hoping that my luck would hold out for another four days, I just scooted those dames into the basement as usual.

As a matter of fact, everything worked fine.

We continued with our novel form of egress for three more

days, and then one evening when I happened to get off a little earlier, I went into the bar to get myself a bicarbonate of soda.

While I was sipping my ambrosia, I suddenly noticed my Peeping Tom friend weaving around in front of half a dozen of his bemused colleagues, and it was quite obvious to me that he was much farther along in liquor than anybody else in that teetering room. As I watched, I saw him clutching at the lapels of one of his fat-faced, bleary-eyed buddies, and I heard him whining a litany that he had probably been repeating pretty frequently during the past three days.

"I tell ya, fellash," he said. "Dish here hotel is got some preddy shnazzy people livin' in it. Preddy, preddy shnazzy, I'm tellin' ya. Dey're so damned shnazzy dey even send deir doidy goils out to be laundered. I sheen 'em meself. I sheen 'em wid me own eyes, I tell ya, fellash; dose doidy goils go straight down wid de doidy laundry and get cleaned up—'cause I sheen 'em wid me own eyes. I offer to bet anybody a case of bourbon dat I sheen what I sheen! I tell ya, fellash, I sheen what I sheen!"

And then I realized the answer to the seemingly great mystery, why none of these vandals had been bothering us. You see, even among those freewheeling lushes this creature was such an outstandingly tanked-up disaster that nobody believed one word he said.

So, without any further extraneous problems to bedevil us, we proceeded to prepare our creation for its New York opening, where the critics were all ready and waiting for us, and where, within a very short time, they quite justifiably bombed us right out of existence.

CHAPTER SEVENTEEN

W<small>HEN I CAME</small> back from Europe, after having visited Father Joseph, I decided to go to the Public Health Service Hospital in Lexington, Kentucky, in order to get cured of my drug addiction.

I knew very little about this place, but I signed myself in as a volunteer patient, and only after I had landed there did I discover it was also a federal prison where people were serving sentences up to fifteen years.

In short, I met over a thousand addicts who had largely used heroin and who, professionally, had devoted most of their lives to stealing and, whenever possible, to pimping. There were about three hundred ladies in another section of the hospital who, in their public roles, were often shoplifters or prostitutes or both.

Also among those patients there was a surprising percentage of physicians and nurses, who had acquired their disastrous habits through their facile proximity to drugs, and I discovered, somewhat later on, that permanent recovery among these victims was much greater than among the rest of the individuals in that place.

In any event, I already knew that hustling for dope was a tragically relentless job, but here it became evident to me that these poor, uneducated, and very often psychically unbalanced creatures simply had to steal or pimp or prostitute themselves, since the unlawful purchase of narcotics is surely one of the most expensive vices that modern man can possibly indulge himself in.

So, here they were, more or less patiently biding their time and just hoping for the day when they could once more go out into the streets to start the whole insane round of frustration all over again, almost exactly at the same point where they had left off.

It was surely not a very encouraging picture.

Incidentally, if you are as curious about people as *I* am, then a stay at Lexington is certainly not an altogether worthless experience. I did a good deal of concentrated listening, and as a result I discovered a great many new aspects of life for which nothing in my past had any parallels to offer.

First of all, I had never known that heroin is purchased from "pushers" who, after countless adulterations of the original substance, sell this stuff in small paper decks at ruinous prices to people who are certainly in no position to do any haggling. Since these pushers are in constant danger of being picked up by the cops, they have to be forever on the qui vive and, to the despair of their frantically agitated customers, they often fail to show up even at their most carefully stipulated places of assignation. I also became aware of the fact that heroin users were always obliged to carry a spoon in which their poison could be dissolved in water, and that the resulting mixture had to be heated over flame, and subsequently strained through some absorbent cotton, before it could be safely injected into the bloodstream.

A mess, in short.

I just want you to keep in mind the basic essentials of this horrible business, for it will greatly enhance your understanding of the story I am about to tell you. In other words, you have to have *heroin*, you have to have a *spoon*, and you certainly have to have *water*.

Incidentally, I think it might also be useful for you to grasp the general socioethical climate in this joint. You see, drug addiction breeds a special subculture, whose behavioristic patterns are as firmly adhered to as are the mores which condition the members of the A.M.A. In fact, I very soon discovered that almost all criminals have one thing in common with all doctors: they absolutely won't squeal on each other. To do so is considered an act of such total degradation that it hardly bears thinking about.

Now then, another one of the primary tenets of junkie good manners is never to ask any questions about an addict's past. The assumption seems to be that it will all come out in good time, and that undue inquisitiveness is a sure sign of being square. The odium attached to squareness is very difficult to live down, since it invariably carries certain comic implications which a serious junkie (and all junkies are serious) doesn't like to have associated with his public image.

Indeed, I have found that there is almost a Stone Age pretense of imperturbable stoicism current in criminal circles, and this condition eventually became my most potent ally in defending myself against some of these truculent barnacles. If ever I felt myself unduly harassed or pressured by one of the patients at the hospital, I would simply start to poke fun at him or hang an easily remembered nickname onto his person, and such a maneuver never failed to bring even the toughest customers into line. You may well wonder why they didn't just bop me one on the noggin. Well, that wouldn't have been kosher either, since it would have exposed them to the charge of being thin-skinned, and to be easily upset by mere verbal horseplay would have been considered a sign of insufficient manliness.

That's how I survived.

At any rate, one morning at breakfast, I noticed two newcomers in my special section of the dining room, and if I had ever planned to cast a movie about Sing Sing or San Quentin or Alcatraz, I would instantly have picked those two characters as the ultimate archetypes that are generally associated with such institutions.

Later on, while we were having a short postprandial recess, I moved over to an empty seat beside these aged freshmen and, in violation of every junkie code, I asked them point-blank what they were in for.

"Well," said the stouter and shorter one of the two, "we ain't in fer nuttin', rightly, dis time. We're volunteers."

It goes without saying that the dozen or so *bravos* who were sitting close enough to overhear us were, of course, profoundly disgusted by my intrusive behavior. Even so, I noticed that the ones within my immediate view were quite unable to suppress their obvious astonishment when they heard that these deeply scarred veterans had come into Lexington under their own power. "Had broken *into* the joint," as it was locally phrased.

They certainly were a couple of strange-looking specimens. The tall, thin one, who looked like a much banged-up mummy, had only one leg. The short, fat one seemed like a very fair-skinned man who had been overexposed to a great deal of tropical sunlight; also, he was lugging around such an enormous belly that he was unable to get close enough to the table to properly tackle his grub. I'd noticed that he'd held his plate under his chin while he'd been shoveling away at his hominy grits, and most of his shirtfront was still completely aslop with the various remainders of his breakfast.

But what really gave them away in our company was the fact that their eyeglasses and their false teeth were definitely of prison origins. When anybody spends a year in jail he's entitled to get free specs, and if he's in for a deuce or more, he can also have dentures at the state's expense. Now, what I'm telling you is that every single living soul in that institution could instantly have told you that those blinders and those choppers had been federally issued.

So there was no question that they had done time *somewhere;* the question was just *where.*

"My name is Mike Bronson," the fat one continued, "and dis is my buddy, Rafe Hodges. We're outta Wash't'n."

"Rafe's crutch is just hollow tubing," I said. "You didn't manage to sneak anything in, did you?"

"Naw," said Rafe. "Dey bloo hot air troo dem pipes afore dey give 'em back to me. Ain't much chance o' passin' nuttin' in here. Dey even shove a rubber finger up my ass ta see if I wuz clean."

"That's called a finger wave," I said. "You boys going to stay for a whole cure or are you going to cut out as soon as you feel a little better?"

"Naw," said Mike. "I'm stayin' fer de woiks. I had my enough of it on de street fer a while."

"Me, too," said Rafe. "I ain't studyin' to bust outta here nohow."

"You're smart," I said. "But most of the guys who are volunteers—which means they can leave any time they feel like it—just stay long enough until their withdrawal symptoms get really bad; then off they go looking for a connection."

"Yeah, I know," said Rafe. "When you got dat key in yer pocket, ya get itchy feet right off. But not us. We had it. We gonna stay right here till all dat poison is out of our system. I'm gonna give dem croakers a chanst to get me straighten out."

By "croakers" he meant doctors, of course. Well, they were surely a most enigmatic couple. Never had two volunteers looked less like volunteers, and I could feel the waves of communal skepticism and amazement beating up against the walls and windows of that hospital dining room.

"How come," I said, "that the two of you got so disgusted with the street? I mean, you look like a couple of real old-timers who certainly must know how to handle yourselves."

"We're old-timers, all right," said Mike. "I been on junk nigh on fordy-six years, and Rafe, here, been on it almost as long, too; but, ya know, sometimes tings happen and ya can't fight 'em. Some tings just go wrong and wrong till ya gotta feelin' dat evvythin's against ya. And dat's jist what happen to us."

He looked moodily out of the window for a moment and then he went on.

"It happen las' week, dere, when we wuz suppose ta meet our connection and he let us know dat we should wait fer 'im right near de Lincoln Memorial in Wash't'n. He said two o'clock, so we got dere about one-fifteen, 'count of—you know how it is—we wuz all outta stuff an' we wuz kinda anxious to lay our hands on somethin'. So we sit dere in de car, we got an old Chevy; fact is, we drove down here in dat Chevy; got it stored downtown in Lexington right now. So we sit dere in dat car and we starts waitin'. When it got to be tree o'clock, I tought I'm goin' outta my mind, and Rafe here, he was near faintin', what wid de heat an' all. Well, I tought to myself, when dat son of a bitch finely shows up I'm gonna bust his head wide open, dat's what I'm gonna do. Or at least I'm gonna blacken his goddam eyes fer 'im."

"Ya know," said Rafe suddenly, "dat doidy bastard didn' show until half-pass four."

"Dass right," said Mike. "We wuz more dead dan alive when he finely come alongside."

"What did you do to him?" I asked.

"What we do to 'im?" said Rafe. "We tole him he looked great! Tole him de tie he wuz wearin' wuz a real ringer and dat his shoes had real class—dat's what we tole 'im."

All the men around us, who had been listening to this grim little saga, nodded understandingly. It had all happened to them, with one variation or another, and the mood of intense gloom reflected in their faces gave ample testimony that Mike and Rafe were being hearkened to by an audience of their peers, in suffering, at least.

"Well," I said, "but he did finally show up. Did he have anything on him that had been worth waiting for?"

"Yeah," said Mike. "He sold us a small deck fer twelve dollars, an' I tore right over to de Lincoln Memorial to get us a liddle water."

At this point Mike looked sternly into my eyes and I couldn't help feeling that some peculiarly significant and perhaps even momentous truth was about to be enunciated by him.

"Ya know sump'n?" he said in a very somber voice. "Maybe you don't know dis, but dat *Lincoln Memorial ain't got any water!* It ain't got a single drop o' water in it, no place. Ya ever hear sich a ting? All dat taxpayers' money goin' ta support dat crazy buildin', wid all dem lights on it, an' evvythin', an' not a spoonful o' water when a man might jist come ta need it most. How *about* dat?!?"

I heard deeply sympathetic cluckings coming to us from all sides as Mike turned belligerently in all directions in his heart-rending appeal to a defrauded citizenry.

"Ya coulda got some water outta da radiator," somebody in back of me volunteered.

"Yeah, dass what we finely did," said Mike. "It wuz all rusty, too, but we wuz so sick, de bote of us, we couldn't wait no longer. So I got a spoonful o' water an' we opened up dat deck—and den—"

He turned and looked accusingly at Rafe, and that poor cripple slowly lowered his head, as if the shame now about to be unveiled were really too profound for indiscriminate public disclosure.

"You know dat stump o' his?" said Mike, pointing at the stub of Rafe's missing leg. "Well, dey did a bum job on it. It happen at Missouri State, an' de croaker dat sawed it off botched de whole ting, and sometimes it starts jerkin' up an' down, all by itself, like a baby dat's got de colic. Just like dat. Well, when I held dat deck over dat spoon, I'm goddam, if dat stump o' his don't give a jerk an' knock dat whole deck of H right outta my hand. Knocked it right all over dat goddam car, too."

The two men now looked at each other, and the shock of that dreadful event seemed to be as completely alive in their sick hearts as it had been during that dreadful moment when it had actually happened to them. Rafe's eyes, in particular, appeared to have turned inward upon a wilderness of grief too horrible for ordinary mortal contemplation.

The heavy breathing of the silent listeners all around us was clear enough evidence that nobody in that hip crowd felt superior to the victims of that grotesque calamity or considered any aspect of it funny.

"What did you do then?" I finally asked.

"What we do?" said Mike. "We bote got down on our han's and knees, and we starts lickin' dat stuff right off'n dem floorboards—dat's what we did. We jist went on lickin' dem boards till we bote had splinters in our tongues. Later on we ran aroun' like a coupla bitches in high heat, an' dat night we manage ta make anudder score, but it weren't much good. Dat secon' son of a bitch really hung a cruller on us. An' dat's when I say ta Rafe, 'Boy, our luck sure is runnin' out.' It happen to us before, an' we always got desperate an' landed in some preddy tough jams. 'Rafe,' I said, 'let's wrap it up. Let's toin ourself into Lexington while we still movin' under our own power. Rafe,' I said, 'we gotta give our luck a chance ta take a toin.' "

"An' dat's why we're here," said Rafe. "Volunteers. Lookin' fer a liddle break, widout de cops breedin' down de back of our necks fer a change."

"Yeah," said Mike. "You can't fight de breaks. If ya do, yer jist gonna get mangled. I know. I know bedder dan anybody. Bedder dan anybody, except Rafe, maybe."

When I got to know them better, I found out that Mike was sixty-four and Rafe was two years younger. Of course, they had spent the bulk of their lives in various jails all over the country, and one day Mike confided to me that his buddy had been gently reared and that it was his criminal career which had forever cut him off from his family.

"I met his faader oncet, years ago," he said, "an' de old man wuz really nice people. Owned a general store, down Georgia, in a town called Wilfrit. Dead now, de old man. Anyway, when Rafe was a kid he woiked for some pecan people. You know dem pecan growers. Well, one day a feller came along an' offer him a real good job to go up No'th, to Baltimore. So Rafe wen' along, and it toined out lader dat dis guy used to crate a lotta hollow pecans. Bad nuts, ya unnerstan'? He'd just take 'em off de pile o' trash dat de hones' pecan growers would stack up for burnin'. Well, dis goof would put one layer o' good nuts on top of every shipment, an' de rest wuz all hollow ones. One day a buyer happen to open de wrong end an' he had dis guy arrested. Him an' Rafe, who had nuttin' ta do wit it. See? Well, dis guy skipped his bail an' Rafe went to reform school. Dat's how it all started."

"What about you?" I said.

"I didn't get such a good break needer," said Mike. "I wuz woikin' for some son of a bitch who wuz suppose ta sell Easter-egg dyes. Well, he didn't ever really sell any, he jist sent in de orders. Later on, tons o' colors would be shipped ta all sorts o' stores all over evvy place, and den dey foun' out he'd jist collected his commission an' dey weren't no orders no place. I wuz his assistant, so dey grab me, too, an' I couldn' afford a decent mout'piece, so I land in de clink for about sixteen mont'. Dat's de way it woik out fer me. I wuz jist goin' on seventeen den. I'll say one ting fer meself, dough; I wusn' framed offen; I took dam few raps fer odder people. I pulled plenny o' cool jobs on my own accoun', an' de same goes fer Rafe, too."

And now they had made up their minds to lay low in Lexington for a while, until their good fortune would come along once more. As far as I could see, they hadn't had even a halfway decent break of any kind for nearly fifty years; and yet they acted like a couple of big-time operators who suddenly decide to sit out a few rounds, to hold on to their chips until the wheel of fortune, in a somewhat more benign mood, will choose to favor them again.

I believe it was Nietzsche who said, "Each man comes to measure his destiny by the length of his own shadow."

In that case, I can't help wondering about those poor slobs who just go through a long lifetime and, somehow, the sun hardly ever seems to shine on them at all.

My travels to the four selected cities resulted in a background study for both the Justice Department and Congress. Based upon more than 100 interviews conducted during two- to three-week visits to each city, the final report painted a dismal picture of societal response to the elderly victims, despite the documented seriousness of the problem. Public officials within the local criminal justice agencies, social service departments, and aging offices were interviewed, in addition to private and community groups concerned with the problem. It was a very depressing year. Despite the apparent Congressional concern, the impact of the research and the larger National Council of Senior Citizens project, which included seven elderly victim units, appears to be minimal at best.

My final research project has been the central focus of this book and concentrates upon the professional behavior of urban felony court judges. During the past three summers (1980–82) a small sample (50) of judges in three cities—Washington, Philadelphia, and New York (Manhattan)—were thoroughly studied through both observations and interviews. Although at least an additional 50 judges were interviewed and observed as part of my earlier research projects, this was the first time that the judiciary had been the primary focus of my research. The major concern in the most recent endeavor was to assess the process of judicial socialization, to describe their working environment, and to analyze the strains and hardships of their profession.

As noted previously, these accumulated research experiences involve a 12-year period, five projects, 15 cities, and approximately 500 interviews. Breaking the interviews down by type of public official, one finds roughly 100 judges, 200 private criminal lawyers, 50 public defenders, 75 prosecutors, 50 court staff administrators and a mixed group of 35 reporters, professors, community leaders, and police officials. Interviews usually lasted from one to three hours. Although a total of 15 cities were visited for at least a one week period, several were revisited on numerous occasions as indicated in Table 1. Only five cities were visited just once (Miami, Indianapolis, Milwaukee, Denver and Houston). Of those cities visited most

TABLE 1
Cities Visited and Frequency

1–2 Weeks	*3–4 Weeks*	*More than 4 Weeks*
Miami (Crim. Law)	Baltimore	Washington, D.C.
Indianapolis (Bail)	Detroit	Los Angeles
Denver (Crim. Law)	New Orleans	Philadelphia
Houston (Crim. Law)	St. Louis	Chicago
Milwaukee (Aging)	New York	San Francisco/Oakland

CHAPTER EIGHTEEN

———————————————————————————

It is lots of fun to draw pictures and it is a great pain in the neck to do any kind of writing at all.

A painter has the ideal life. I mean a real artist, of course, and not the sick cats who throw paint onto canvas and just wait to see what will happen. But the artist who has learned to control his materials can perform his labors in a room full of people, and the great joy is to see how his work grows from moment to moment until it reaches the point where he finally feels himself reasonably content with what he has produced.

His wife, or his mistress, can drop in from time to time, and he can listen to the comments without in any way jeopardizing his endeavors, since it is his immemorial privilege to ignore what she has to say. She certainly can't possibly disturb him unless he happens to be a very special type of nut altogether.

Writing is agony, mostly, and if you're as experienced as I am you never read a single line you have written to anybody.

At any rate, here are some more drawings.

THE JOINER

He is a member of eight different fraternal organizations.

This means that approximately sixteen times a year he is officially licensed to go on gargantuan binges and that he can make an absolute hog of himself with complete public approval.

Better still, for an equal number of times he is free to get away from that bitch on wheels to whom he is married; that dithering nymphomaniac, his daughter; and that unresponsive, sullen clod who is his son.

Let no man begrudge him his sadly needed and rather sparsely-spaced bacchanalian revels.

After all, he does come back home again, doesn't he?

God only knows *why*.

THE SIRENS

Although I'm not married to any of these broads, I can see them
 in curlers any day at the supermarket, and in Hollywood I've even run into them in this condition at various pretty chic department stores.
It is a drag, isn't it?
I wonder what they could possibly be thinking about?
Actually, I'm not really as puzzled as I'm pretending.
You see, I've got a hunch that these sloppy creatures think themselves so utterly fascinating that they believe they're
 doing us menfolk a great favor by granting us these intimate glimpses into their relentless tussle with their
 recalcitrant hair and their dingy complexions.
So listen, girls, don't bother to give me any treats. Wrestle with
 your physical disadvantages in the privacy of your bed-
 rooms and, in heaven's name, remember to close your
 damned doors!

THE TYRANNOSAURUS

He is not a movie actor made up to resemble some member of an
  extinct species.
He is a living cliché whom I have encountered in Alabama, in
  Georgia, in Mississippi, in the Carolinas—and I don't
  have to tell you that he flourishes in a good many other
  places, including, of course, the state of Louisiana.
He is a walking, breathing horror, who considers himself the
  particular champion of the most revered American
  ways.
What he means by that is the way of the lyncher, the Ku Kluxer
  and all of the other monstrous promoters of strong-arm
  techniques who always seem to know exactly what is
  the best procedure to secure the welfare of the country.
"Suh," he says, "Ah believes in law an' odor!"
He most certainly does, and, what's more, I can smell it all the
  way up here.

THE BAD EGG

This is a sub-teen-ager—thirteen years old, to be exact—and she
    is the sort of catastrophe I can hardly bear to think
    about.
But I *will* tell you something regarding her mother.
That worthy woman is not just permissive.
Don't you believe a word of *that*.
She is a dangerous psychopath who is living out her own sexual
    frustrations by encouraging this young moral cripple
    to go on wild necking parties, in which she herself is
    a proxy participant.
This mother's derivative orgasms at the expense of her child's
    physical and mental equilibrium are a danger to all of
    society, and a truly active communal conscience would
    be as profoundly alarmed by her condition as if she
    were a carrier of the bubonic plague.
I'm not saying anything about the father, because I have never
    in all of my life met a single father who tried to rush
    his early-teen-age girl into a premature involvement
    with boys.
It takes a really sick *woman* to promote that sort of vile maneu-
    ver, and we obviously have more than our share of such
    demented ladies around at this time.

JUST FOLKS

This is Loney Speargrass, the Hootenanny King.
He used to be the doorman at Vince's Vintnery out in San Francisco before he discovered his true vocation.
He doesn't only yammer other people's songs; he makes up quite a number of his own.
As a matter of fact, he has to, because he is so unbelievably stupid he can barely remember the address of the house in which he generally festers.
Since Loney perspires very freely and hardly ever bathes, he has become especially popular with the down-to-earth crowd that feels he is much closer to the soil than the usual run-of-the-mill folk-concertizers.
There can be no possible argument about that.
There just isn't any clay any commoner than Loney.
He's the true dirt, from way, way under.

THE SANITARY SHREW

This is not a Berber tribesman guarding some fiercely contested outpost in the Atlas Mountains, nor is it an Afghan chieftain preparing to rectify the score in a lifelong blood feud.

No.

This is just Mrs. W. W. Whitcomb, bent on a thorough job of housecleaning.

When Mrs. Whitcomb ties a preparatory rag around her head, all judicious citizens instantly take refuge in the nearby cafeterias.

She is, in fact, the lineal descendant of that Mrs. McStinger who settled all of her interfamily hang-ups by rolling out the water pails and inundating her household in a relentless tide of steaming soapsuds.

Her broom closet is an arsenal of deadly weapons, with which she rectifies all of her rampant rancors. The clatter of these seemingly harmless implements can be more alarming than the sound of thundering battle drums.

Her fury, compounded with cold sweat and boiling detergents, is more devastating than the wrath of Vesuvius coupled to that of Krakatoa.

Let mankind beware! And make way for the fiend with the scrub brush!

GUSSIE

Her voice goes through you like a knife.

This is more than just a metaphor, since she has already buried four of her husbands, and the insurance actuaries, in their most secret archives, never fail to underline her name with red ink.

Her laughter is her secret weapon.

Anyone exposed to her cachinnations for any length of time is sure to seek flight either in a sanitarium or in the grave.

When she was still in her teens, her parents took her on a trip to the Grand Canyon. When Gussie, for the sake of the resounding echo, laughed a little louder than usual, the father and mother silently clasped hands and leaped into the abyss.

She hasn't stopped laughing since.

THE PIXIE

She has been a playful little girl for over thirty-eight years.

She paints a little, she sculpts a little, and she is certainly quite knowledgeable on the subject of tea-leaf readings.

Since she is enormously rich, it stands to reason that she always moves in the unqualified approval of an adoring entourage.

Her name is frequently mentioned in connection with prospective theatrical ventures of all sorts, and she occasionally does make rather brief appearances in summer stock.

Her childhood nurse, who is still alive but somewhat ailing, needed an operation just a short while ago, and of course this dear little girl at once lent her the money.

What is more, she made the old woman sign a note guaranteeing her four percent interest on the six hundred dollars she had advanced her.

She is a real dilettante in many matters, excepting only, as you can plainly see, in the most *essential* things.

CHAPTER NINETEEN

THIS CHAPTER IS definitely not for people who read my books mostly for the yaks they provide. So, for those who drape expectant smiles on their faces whenever they reach for anything I have written, my advice is this: You will be much better off if you skip the next few pages completely.

You see, I've come at last to the point where I want to offer a few brief excerpts from the books I am now reading. A great number of people have written me about this, and I have told them that while my reading habits were extremely erratic, I would, in some future installment of my autobiography, give some hints as to the nature of the writing which had particular fascination for me at this time.

Incidentally, I might as well confess that I have always had rather strong opinions about authors who filled their books with other people's literary efforts. Well, at this juncture it seems not only relevant but rather crucial for me to give up the bulk of this chapter to a small sampling from my current reading itinerary, and I have justified this to myself by making this book, compensationally, just a little longer than usual.

First of all, let me tell you something about Jane Welsh Carlyle. She was, of course, the wife of Thomas Carlyle, whose full-length portrait was even painted by the great James McNeill Whistler.

Thomas was something of an intellectual titan during his own lifetime, but, as far as I can determine, hardly anybody nowadays reads him at all.

At any rate, Jane Welsh was the only daughter of a Scottish physician, who adored and spoiled his precocious jewel just exactly as I would if I had been lucky enough to sire such a phenomenon. It goes without saying that great expectations were cherished regarding her unquestionably brilliant future, but then one day, in the midst of all these domestic felicities, the father suddenly died.

Poor Mrs. Welsh, the doctor's widow, did her utmost to continue in the pattern set by her late husband, and she viewed with deep misgivings the great number of eager suitors who proceeded to besiege her home with the intent of spiriting away her witty and unusually charming offspring.

The siege of the prospective bridegrooms lasted for quite a spell, and then, one afternoon in the late summer, a man called Thomas Carlyle settled his long, bony frame into an armchair beside a book-filled wall of their cozy drawing room.

It was a truly momentous visit. Carlyle was no fool. He did not fail to realize the high worth of the nimble-tongued girl who twitted him playfully about his scholastic awkwardnesses, and we know that after his departure he came to write her long and extremely persuasive letters about the pathetic state of his loneliness as a mere bachelor.

She answered him in a tone of teasing amiability which, I'm sorry to say, soon changed to something a good deal warmer, and after not too long a time they were finally engaged to be married.

It was the mistake of her life.

I don't know what she could have done; I just have the feeling that she should have waited for me. I say this because I am one of the very few people in the whole world who would have known how to love her as she deserved to be. You cannot possibly imagine how fond I have become of this woman over the years, and I can assure you that there is hardly a scrap of paper which bears her handwriting which I have not, somehow or another, managed to read with feelings of compassionate involvement.

Actually, she stands first among the dear gifted ladies who lived and languished and died before my time.

I must confess that I never cared much for Helen of Troy, and I really wouldn't give you two cents for the privilege of making her acquaintance. After all, she was a fathead, a bed-rabbit with international inclinations; and I'm quite sure that in anything but a horizontal position she must have been an overwhelming bore.

But Jane Welsh Carlyle and Emily Dickinson and Emily Brontë have been my precious darlings ever since the very first time I learned of their existence.

There are a few others abroad in the shadowy lands besides these three, of course, but it would lead us too far astray to pursue this course in my grapho-amorous predilections and at this very pressing moment I really can't spare the time for the inspection of such an enchanting postmortem seraglio.

So, let us get on.

I think you ought to know that Thomas Carlyle's closest friend and literary executor, a man called James Anthony Froude, confessed in a published biography that his hero was sexually impotent. Naturally, a great many legends and anecdotes have grown in fungoid fluorescence around this deplorable condition, and I will now tell you the one I choose to believe above all the others.

It is told that on their wedding night the belching bridegroom (he was chronically constipated and dyspeptic) entered his wife's boudoir with the heroic intent of consummating his nuptial pledges—or of "finalizing his marriage," as the advertising people would say.

And then, whatever the hell happened, it is reported that Jane, a healthy and vibrant young bride, permitted herself a short but definitely audible giggle. No sooner had that unfortunate sound passed her embarrassed lips than the gawky groom rose from the hymeneal couch and stalked from her presence out into the cold darkness beyond.

Well, legend has it that for the next forty some years the great Thomas Carlyle never again crossed the threshold of his wife's sleeping chamber.

I firmly believe that this all actually happened.

Such behavior tallies completely with what is known of *his* character, and I am readily persuaded that it was truly my little Jane who indulged herself in the most disastrously far-reaching giggle ever perpetrated by any woman in all of recorded history.

It will not surprise you to learn that later on in their life together she became the victim of many nervous disorders, as well as of blinding migraine headaches, which she suffered through nights of incalculable agony.

We know that Thomas continued right on with his various writing chores, and it is a matter of record that he eventually became a much respected and highly esteemed literary asset to the whole nation.

Curiously enough, he also became pretty closely involved with a lady of title, who, from time to time, even extended the smile of her benign patronage on the deeply mortified Jane.

But enough.

You see, I think Jane Welsh Carlyle was not only a remarkable and desperately injured person but also, above all else, a most gifted writer, whose letters are a treasure-house in which I never weary of searching for particularly scintillant gems of uniquely feminine perceptions.

I give you, first, one of the letters which she wrote to a woman who had sent her some samples of home-cooked poetry. Read this letter slowly and carefully, since it is, in its way, a kind of masterpiece.

Incidentally, her reference to Benvenuto Cellini has to do with a statue of Perseus which that sculptor had once been casting in the days of the high Renaissance. Cellini, who was, for the most part of his life, a carver and molder of comparatively small gold and silver objects, had for this one time set his mind upon creating a comparatively large statue of the mythological hero Perseus. But since the size of this sculpture was not at all along the familiar pattern of his usual work, he had totally miscalculated the amount of metal that was required for a successful casting. It was then, during this extreme emergency, that Cellini threw all the available jewels and precious trinkets in his studio helter-skelter into the quickly cooling mold, lest the success of his enterprise be endangered by the mere lack of sufficient raw materials.

And now here is her letter:

To Miss Mary Smith,
    Carlisle

5 Cheyne Row,
Chelsea.
January 11th, 1857.

Dear Miss Smith,

This time you come to me as an old acquaintance whom I am glad to shake hands with again. The mere fact of your being still in the same position after so long an interval, and with such passionate inward protest as that first letter indicated, is a more authentic testimony of your worth, than if you had sent me a certificate of character signed by all the clergy and householders of Carlisle! So many talents are wasted, so many enthusiasms turned to smoke, so many lives blighted for want of a little patience and endurance, for want of understanding and laying to heart that which you have so well expressed in these verses—the meaning of the Present—for want of recognizing that it is not the greatness or littleness of "the duty nearest at hand," but the spirit in which one does it, that makes one's doing noble or mean!

I can't think how people who have any natural ambition, and any sense of power in them, escape going mad in a world like this, without the recognition of that! I know I was very near mad when I found it out for myself (as one has to find out for oneself everything that is to be of any real practical use to one). Shall I tell you how it came into my head? Perhaps it may be of comfort to you in similar moments of fatigue and disgust.

I had gone with my husband to live on a little estate of peat bog, that had descended to me, all the way down from John Welsh, the Covenanter, who married a daughter of John Knox. That didn't, I'm ashamed to say, make me feel Craigenputtock a whit less of a peat bog, and a most dreary, untoward place to live at. In fact, it was sixteen miles distant on every side from all the conveniences of life—shops, and even post office!

Further, we were very poor and, further and worst, being an only child, and brought up to "great prospects," I was sublimely ignorant of every branch of useful knowledge, though a capital Latin scholar and a very fair mathematician!! It behoved me in these astonishing circumstances to learn—to sew! Husbands, I was shocked to find, wore their stockings into holes! and were always losing buttons! and I was expected to "look to all that." Also, it behoved me to learn to cook! No capable servant choosing to live at "such an out of the way place," and my husband having "bad digestion" which complicated my difficulties dreadfully. The bread above all, brought from Dumfries, "soured on his stomach" (oh Heavens!); and it was plainly my duty as a Christian wife to bake at home! So I sent for Cobbett's "Cottage Economy" and fell to work at a loaf of bread. But knowing nothing of the process of fermentation or the heat of ovens, it came to pass that my loaf got put into the oven at the time myself ought to have put into bed, and I remained the only person not asleep, in a house in the middle of a desert! One o'clock struck, and then two and then three; and aching with weariness, my heart aching with a sense of forlornness and degradation—"That I who had been so petted at home, whose comfort had been studied by everybody in the house, who had never been required to do anything but cultivate my mind, should have to pass all those hours of the night watching a loaf of bread! which mightn't turn out bread after all!"

Such thoughts maddened me, till I laid my head on the table and sobbed aloud. It was then that somehow the idea of Benvenuto Cellini's sitting up all night watching his Perseus in the oven, came into

233

my head; and suddenly I asked myself, "After all, in the sight of the upper powers, what is the mighty difference between a statue of Perseus and a loaf of bread, so that each be the thing one's· hand hath found to do? The man's determined will, his energy, his patience, his resources, were the really admirable things, of which the statue of Perseus was the mere chance expression. If he had been a woman living at Craigenputtock, with a dyspeptic husband, sixteen miles from a baker, and he a bad one, all these same qualities would have come out most fitting in a good loaf of bread!"

I cannot express what consolation this germ of an idea spread over an uncongenial life, during five years we lived at that savage place; where my two immediate predecessors had gone mad, and the third had taken to drink.

Yours truly,
JANE W. CARLYLE.

The next three letters are addressed to her husband. The first one contains some of her rare complaints and the others will give you a pretty good idea of the sort of imaginative, deeply devoted wife she was. Thomas was obviously planning a trip to the Continent without her and had written her an urgent note about forwarding him his passport.

The fourth letter contains an account of her visit to the income-tax collector's office and the last one is addressed to an old friend who had known her since earliest childhood.

To Thomas Carlyle
    The Gill.

5 Cheyne Row,
Chelsea.
Friday, June 25th, 1858.

Don't let your enjoyment of "the Country" be disturbed by thoughts of me still "in Town." I won't stay here longer than I find it good for me. But what I feel to need at present is, above all things human and divine, rest from "mental worry"; and nowhere is there such fair outlook of that for me as just at home under the present conditions. "The cares of Bread" have been too heavy for me lately; and the influx of "cousins" most wearing; and to see you constantly discontented, and as much so with me, apparently, as with all other things, when I have neither the strength and spirits to bear up against your discontent, nor the obtuseness to be indifferent to it—that has done me more harm than you have the least notion of. You have not the least notion what a killing thought it is to have put into one's heart, gnawing there day and night, that one ought to be dead, since one can no longer make the same exertions as formerly; that one was taken "for better," not by any means "for worse"; and, in fact, that the only feasible and dignified thing that remains for one to do is to just die, and be done with it.

Better, if possible, to recover some health of body and mind, you say. Well, yes: if possible. In that view I go with Neuberg this evening to view a field of hay. . . .

To Thomas Carlyle
The Gill

Chelsea.
Thursday, July 29th, 1858.

Oh, my dear, my dear! What did you do with the key of your bureau? There is no vestige of a passport in the upper "little drawer next the fire," the only drawer which is unlocked; the keys used to lie in that. I have wasted the whole morning in seeking a key to open the top part, or another drawer where the keys may be, and have found only two of your lost dog-whistles! I don't like to have the locks picked until it is hopeless finding the key. If you have it or know where you put it, and tell me by Saturday morning, there would just be time to send the passport before I start; but, as I tell you, my morning is all wasted, and in the afternoon I must go up to Piccadilly to get some indispensable little items for my visit. I have been kept back these last two days by the coldness of the weather, and my extreme sensitiveness. The prospect of going a journey and living in another person's house is doing me more harm than probably the reality will do; I could "scream at the idea of it" sometimes, and write off, "Oh, you must excuse me!" But again, just the more I feel nervous, the more I need to try anything that may brace my nerves; and, of course, a doctor would tell me to get rid of this incessant little dry cough "before October." I should not say incessant, for in the forenoons, when I hold my tongue, I hardly cough at all—at least it is quite another sort of cough, bringing up phlegm at intervals; but in the evening, especially if anyone comes, it is as incessant as the chirp of my adopted sparrow. I am not getting weaker, however, except in my mind. I take exercise every day, "chiefly in an omnibus, Mr. Carlyle!" And I try every day to do or see something cheering; I should soon fall into melancholy mania if I didn't. Last evening, for example, I had old Mrs. Larkin to tea— such a pretty little rough tea, you can't fancy, and Mrs. Larkin was so pleased. And I had Mrs. Hawkes to talk to them, and George Cooke came accidentally. George Cooke is very attentive and sympathetic to me. But the key, the key!

Yours affectionately,
JANE CARLYLE

To Thomas Carlyle,
The Gill.

Friday, July 30th, 1858.

Here it is Dear! I found I was going to have no peace if I waited till Saturday on the chance of your remembering where you put it, which was as good as no chance at all! So, after another fruitless search, I sent for Hacking to pick the lock. But "Providence did show some little mercy" (as Grace Macdonald said when her arm was broken and not the glass of her watch); Hacking brought with him a bag full of keys, one of which opened the top, shallow drawer, and in that lay the key of the top part—The passport was in one of the pigeon holes. Hacking said it was too good a lock to have spoiled with picking and that one might have tried a thousand keys without getting one to fit —so you see there was "some little mercy"—But yesterday was doomed to be a day devoted to the intolerable business of seeking lost keys! Before calling in Hacking, I had collected all the keys in the house to try on these drawers; amongst the rest the key of my portmanteau, and that one (to be needed on Saturday) in a manner altogether mysterious, "brankraipit and gaid oot of sicht" and I was driven so desperate with the fag and worry of seeking it next—that I ordered a new key; to escape recommencing on the morrow!

Won't your Passport require to be viséd? . . .

Yours ever,

JANE W. CARLYLE.

DEAR FRIEND,

I have been fretting inwardly all this day at the prospect of having to go and appeal before the Tax Commissioners at Kensington to-morrow morning. Still, it must be done. If Mr. Carlyle should go him-self, he would run his head against some post in his impatience; and besides, for me, when it is over it will be over, whereas he would not get the better of it for twelve months—if ever at all.

O me miseram! not one wink of sleep the whole night through! so great the "rale mental agony in my own inside" at the thought of that horrid appealing. It was with feeling like the ghost of a dead dog, that I rose and dressed and drank my coffee, and then started for Kensington. Mr. C. said "the voice of honour seemed to call on him to go himself." But either it did not call loud enough, or he would not listen to that charmer. I went in a cab, to save all my breath for ap-pealing. Set down at 30 Hornton Street, I found a dirty private-like house, only with Tax Office painted on the door. A dirty woman-servant opened the door, and told me the Commissioners would not be there for half-an-hour, but I might walk up. There were already some half-score of men assembled in the waiting-room, among whom I saw the man who cleans our clocks, and a young apothecary of Cheyne Walk. All the others, to look at them, could not have been suspected for an instant, I should have said, of making a hundred a year. Feeling in a false position, I stood by myself at a window and "thought shame" (as children say). Men trooped in by twos and threes, till the small room was pretty well filled; at last a woman showed herself. "O my!" did I ever know the full value of any sort of woman—as woman—before! By this time some benches had been brought in, and I was sitting nearest the door. The woman sat down on the same bench with me, and, misery acquainting one with strange bedfellows, we entered into conversation without having been intro-

237

duced, and I had "the happiness," as Allan termed it, "of seeing a woman more miserable than myself." Two more women arrived at intervals, one a young girl of Dundee, "sent by my uncle that's ill"; who looked to be always recapitulating inwardly what she had been told to say to the Commissioners. The other, a widow, and such a goose, poor thing; she was bringing an appeal against no overcharge in her individual paper, but against the doubling of the Income Tax. She had paid the double tax once, she said, because she was told they would take her goods for it if she didn't—and it was so disgraceful for one in a small business to have her goods taken; besides it was very disadvantageous; but now that it was come round again she would give up. She seemed to attach an irresistible pathos to the title of widow, this woman. "And me a widow, ma'am," was the winding up of her every paragraph. The men seemed as worried as the women, though they put a better face on it, even carrying on a sort of sickly laughing and bantering with one another. "First-come lady," called the clerk, opening a small side-door, and I stept forward into a grand peut-être. There was an instant of darkness while the one door was shut behind and the other opened in front; and there I stood in a dim room where three men sat around a large table spread with papers. One held a pen ready over an open ledger; another was taking snuff, and had taken still worse in his time, to judge by his shaky, clayed appearance. The third, who was plainly the cock of that dungheap, was sitting for Rhadamanthus—a Rhadamanthus without the justice. "Name," said the horned-owl-looking individual holding the pen. "Carlyle." "What?" "Carlyle." Seeing he still looked dubious, I spelt it for him. "Ha!" cried Rhadamanthus, a big, bloodless-faced, insolent-looking fellow. "What is this? why is Mr. Carlyle not come himself? Didn't he get a letter ordering him to appear? Mr. Carlyle wrote some nonsense about being exempted from coming, and I desired an answer to be sent that he must come, must do as other people." "Then, sir," I said, "your desire has been neglected, it would seem, my husband having received no such letter; and I was told by one of your fellow Commissioners that Mr. Carlyle's personal appearance was not indispensable." "Huffgh! Huffgh! what does Mr. Carlyle mean by saying he has no income from his writings, when he himself fixed it in the beginning at a hundred and fifty?" "It means, sir, that in ceasing to write, one ceases to be paid for writing, and Mr. Carlyle has published nothing for several years." "Huffgh! Huffgh! I understand nothing about that." "I do," whispered the snuff-taking Commissioner at my ear. "I quite understand a literary man does not always make money. I would take it all off, for my share, but (sinking his voice still lower) I am only one voice here, and not the most important." "There," said I, handing to Rhadamanthus Chapman and Hall's account, "that will prove Mr. Carlyle's statement." "What am I to make of that? Huffgh! we should have Mr. Carlyle here to swear to this before we believe it." "If a gentleman's word of honour written at the bottom of that is not enough, you can put me on my oath; I am ready to swear to it!" "You! you indeed! No, no! we can do nothing with your oath!" "But, sir, I understand my husband's affairs fully, better than he does himself." "That I can well believe; but we can make nothing of this," flinging my document contemptuously on the table. The horned owl picked it up, glanced over it while Rhadamanthus was tossing papers about, and grumbling about "people that wouldn't conform to rules"; then handed it back to him, saying deprecatingly: "But, sir, this is a very plain statement." "Then what has Mr. Carlyle to live upon? You don't mean to tell me he lives on that?" pointing to the document. "Heaven forbid, sir! but I am not here to explain what Mr. Carlyle has to live on, only to declare his income from Literature during the last three years." "True! true!" mumbled the not-most-important voice at my elbow, "Mr. Carlyle, I believe, has landed income." "Of which," said I haughtily, for my spirit was up, "I have fortunately no account to render in this kingdom and to this board." "Take off fifty pounds, say a hundred—take off a hundred pounds," said Rhadamanthus to the horned owl. "If we write Mr. Carlyle down a hundred and fifty he has no reason to complain, I think. There, you may go. Mr. Carlyle has no reason to complain."

Second-come woman was already introduced, and I was motioned to the door; but I could not depart without saying that "at all events there was no use in complaining, since they had the power to enforce *their decision.*" On stepping out, my first thought was, what a mercy Carlyle didn't come himself! For the rest, though it might have gone better, I was thankful that it had not gone worse. When one has been threatened with a great injustice, one accepts a smaller as a favour.

Oh Betty! do you remember the little green thing I left in your care while I was over in Fife? And when I returned you had transplanted it into a yellow glass, which I have on my toilet table to this hour, keeping my rings etc. in it. Well! I must surely have told you long ago that the little thing, with two tiny leaves, from my father's grave, had, after twelve months in the garden at Chelsea, declared itself a gooseberry bush! It has gone on flourishing, in spite of want of air and soil, and is now the prettiest round bush, quite full of leaves. I had several times asked our old gardener if there was nothing one could do to get the bush to bear, if it were only one gooseberry; but he treated the case as hopeless. "A poor wild thing. No, if you want to have gooseberries, ma'am, better get a proper gooseberry bush in its place." The old Goth! He can't be made to understand that things can have any value but just their garden value. He once, in spite of all I could beg and direct, rooted out a nettle I had brought from Crawford Churchyard, and with infinite pains got to take root and flourish. But, I was going to tell you, one day Lizzy, my youngest maid, came running in from the garden to ask me had I seen the three little gooseberries on the gooseberry bush? I rushed out, excited as a child, to look at them, and there they were—three little gooseberries, sure enough! And immediately I had settled it in my mind to send one of them in a letter when full grown. But, alas! whether it was through too much staring at them, or too much east wind, or through mere delicacy in "the poor wild thing," I can't tell; only the result, that the three bits of gooseberries, instead of growing larger, grew every day less, till they reached the smallness of pinheads, and then dropped on the ground! I could have cried when the last one went.

Incidentally, it was Jane Welsh Carlyle who was the original subject of a poem written by Leigh Hunt, called "Jenny Kissed Me."

JENNY KISSED ME

Jenny kissed me when we met,
  Jumping from the chair she sat in;
Time, you thief, who love to get
  Sweets into your list, put that in!
Say I'm weary, say I'm sad,
  Say that health and wealth have missed me,
Say I'm growing old, but add,
  Jenny kissed me.

So much for Jane Welsh Carlyle; may the earth rest gently on her sprightly bones.

The next group of letters was written by Emily Dickinson, America's greatest woman poet. I have adored her for many, many years, and I'm happy to say that her reputation, in my own lifetime, has grown so secure that any reasonably literate person must surely be familiar with at least some measure of her work. After all, it is constantly being quoted, all over the place, by a good many lesser people, and new editions of her poems are available in an endless variety of reprints.

Her legend, too, has become quite well known.

She was a New England spinster whose emotional attachments seemed concentrated almost exclusively on her immediate family and her not very large circle of corresponding friends. Oddly enough, this is true only to a very small degree, since the incalculable intuitions of her genius provided her with more than apt surmises on the joys and agonies rampant in the whole wide world. She frequently appears to be more totally aware of the questions and contradictions palpitating in the restless heart of mankind than a good many people who were functioning at the very vortex of its most concentrated activities.

Some time before her middle years, Emily voluntarily sequestered herself in her father's house and was known only as a fleeting ghost to those very few who accidentally happened to catch a brief glimpse of her. She never went out into the streets again, and yet she left behind her a body of work which never fails to capture even the subtlest fluctuations of nature and quite frequently she displays the icily disenchanted convictions which one generally associates with the findings of the most objective philosophical intelligences.

She was a real enigma—a true miracle, whose starched white dress was constantly disappearing around the corner. Offhand, I can't think of a single soul who so passionately and with so much sympathetic understanding loved all the multiple manifestations of life on this earth, and I shall certainly go on worshiping her precious memory as long as my own span of existence will last.

The first letter which I submit to you was not written by Emily at all; it was sent by a Mrs. Todd to her parents in Washington, D.C. This lady, a recent arrival in Amherst, informs her relatives on her newly formed impressions of this small community.*

I must tell you about the character of Amherst. It is a lady whom the people call the Myth. She is a sister of Dickinson, & seems to be the climax of all the family oddity. She has not been outside of her own house in fifteen years, except once to see a new church, when she crept out at night, & viewed it by moonlight. No one who calls upon her mother & sister ever see her, but she allows little children once in a great while, & one at a time, to come in, when she gives them cake or candy, or some nicety, for she is very fond of little ones. But more often she lets down the sweetmeat by a string, out of a window, to them. She dresses wholly in white, & her mind is said to be perfectly wonderful. She writes finely, but no one ever sees her. Her sister, who was at Mrs. Dickinson's party, invited me to come & sing to her mother sometime. . . . People tell me that the myth will hear every note—she will be near, but unseen. . . . Isn't that like a book? So interesting.

* All these letters have been taken from *The Years and Hours of Emily Dickinson*, by Jay Leyda, © 1960 by Yale University Press, Inc.

No one knows the cause of her isolation, but of course there are dozens of reasons assigned.

This is a letter by Emily Dickinson to John L. Graves:

Amherst, April 27th

It is Sunday—now—John—and all have gone to church—the wagons have done passing, and I have come out in the new grass to listen to the anthems.

Three or four Hens have followed me, and we sit side by side—and while they crow and whisper, I'll tell you what I see today, and what I would that you saw—

You remember the crumbling wall that divides us from Mr. Sweetser, and the crumbling elms and evergreen, and other crumbling things—that spring, and fade, and cast their bloom within a simple twelvemonth— . . . And here are Robins—just got home—and giddy Crows—and Jays—and will you trust me—as I live, here's a bumble-bee —not such as summer brings—John—earnest, manly bees—but a kind of a Cockney, dressed in jaunty clothes . . . then there are sadder features—here and there, wings half gone to dust, that fluttered so, last year—a mouldering plume, an empty house, in which a bird resided. Where last year's flies, their errand ran, and last year's crickets fell! We, too, are flying—fading, John—and the song "here lies," soon upon lips that loves us now—will have hummed and ended.

To live, and die, and mount again in triumphant body, and next time, try the upper air—is no schoolboy's theme! It is a jolly thought to think that we can be eternal—when air and earth are full of lives that are gone and done—and a conceited thing indeed, this promised Resurrection! . . . .

Emily Dickinson sends Mrs. Sarah Tuckerman a pressed dandelion tied with scarlet ribbon:

The Dandelion's pallid Tube
Astonished the Grass

And Winter instantly becomes
An infinite Alas
The Tube uplifts a signal bud
And then a shouting Flower
And proclamation of the suns
That sepulture is o'er

Early May 1870 Emily Dickinson writes to Louise and Frances Norcross in Milwaukee:

This little sheet of paper has lain for several years in my Shakespeare, and though it is blotted and antiquated is endeared by its resting-place.

I always thing of you peculiarly in May, as it is the peculiar anniversary of your loving kindness to me, though you have always been dear cousins, and blessed me all you could. . . .

Maggie is ironing, and a cotton and linen and ruffle heat makes the pussy's cheeks red. It is lonely without the birds today, for it rains badly, and the little poets have no umbrellas. . . .

Emily Dickinson to Mrs. Holland, October 15, 1881: "One who only said I am sorry helped me the most when Father ceased—it was too soon for language."

And now, to wind up this section, I give you a series of letters written by an eighteenth-century French author. The following pages contain excerpts from an *imaginary* correspondence, called *Persian Letters*, composed by a man called Montesquieu, who was a wit and a social critic of considerable acerbity and distinction.

Montesquieu decided to cloak the irony of his message under the pretense that some learned, aristocratic visitors from Persia had come to investigate the cultural conditions of western Europe and that they were writing to each other, as well as to their friends back home, about the nature of their various travel experiences.

It is not at all surprising that after a little while these explora-tory Asians arrive at the opinion that not only human life but also social conditions in general were really ordered much more sensibly and satisfactorily in their native Ispahan.

For an ordinary writer, such a summation would, indeed, have been quite enough. He would have expatiated freely on the hypo-crisies and iniquities rampant all over the Christian world and he would have drawn his devastating conclusions at the expense of his own national contemporaries.

But Montesquieu was more than just a writer; he was an artist. And, so, when you have finished reading his last letter you will find that there ain't no balm in Gilead, but there ain't no balm in Ispahan neither.

I'm sorry that in such a brief selection I am unable to include a great deal of correspondence relating to the special shenanigans rampant in the harems of Persia. But, after all, I can only provide you with a tiny sampling of all the goodies stuck away in the total pudding; the rest you will just have to discover for your-self.

Here are the letters:

USBEK TO HIS FAVORITE WIFE, ROXANA
AT THE SERAGLIO IN ISPAHAN

How happy you are, Roxana, to be living in the sweet land of Persia, and not in those corrupted countries where modesty and virtue are unknown! Happy Roxana! you dwell in my seraglio as in some abode of innocence impregnable to the assaults of mankind. It delights you to think that your fortunate disability insures you against the risk of falling. Never has a man sullied your innocence with a lascivious look; not even your father-in-law has seen your lovely mouth on those festal occasions when a certain amount of freedom is permitted, for you have never failed to cover it with a sacred veil. Happy Roxana! in the country, you have always had eunuchs to walk before you, ready to kill the audacious wretch who did not fly at your approach. What difficulty did not I myself, to whom Heaven sent you for my felicity, experience in mastering that treasure which you defended with such firmness! What an affliction it was for me not to see you during the first days of our marriage! And what impatience was mine when I did see you! You did not gratify it, however; you irritated it, on the contrary, by the stubborn refusals of an alarmed chastity; you confounded me with all those other men from whom you conceal yourself on every occasion. Do you remember the day when I lost you among your slaves, who betrayed me and frustrated my efforts to discover you? Do you remember that other day when, seeing that your tears were powerless, you appealed to the authority of your mother to check the fury of my love? Do you remember how, when all these resources failed you, you found others in your courageous soul? You seized a dagger and threatened to immolate the husband that loved you, if he persisted in requiring from you that which you cherished even more than you did him. Two months passed in this combat between love and virtue. You pushed your chaste scruples too far; you refused to surrender even after being vanquished, and defended to the last an expiring virginity; you regarded me as an enemy who outraged you, not as a spouse who adored you; for more than three months you never dared to lift your eyes to me without blushing; your air of confusion seemed to reproach me for the advantage I had taken. I did not even enjoy a tranquil possession; you robbed me of all the charms and graces you could, and I was intoxicated by the greatest favors though I could not obtain the least.

If you had been reared in this country, you would not have been thrown into such agitation; the women here have lost all restraint; they appear before men with their faces uncovered, as if they courted defeat; they seek to attract their eyes; they let their looks dwell upon them in the mosques, on the promenades, and even in their very homes; the service of eunuchs is unknown. Instead of the noble simplicity and charming bashfulness which reign amongst you, a brutal shamelessness prevails, to which it is impossible for me to grow accustomed.

Yes, Roxana, if you were here you would feel outraged at the ignominious condition into which your sex has sunk; you would fly those abominable places, and would sigh for the sweet retreat wherein you find happiness, where you are safe from yourself, where no danger terrifies you, and, in fine, where you can love me without ever fearing to lose that love which it is your duty to feel for me.

When you heighten the brilliancy of your complexion with the most beautiful colors; when you perfume your body with the most precious essences; when you appear in your loveliest garments; when you try to distinguish yourself from your companions by the grace with which you dance and the sweetness with which you sing; in a word, when you attempt to rival them in charms, amiability, and sprightliness, I cannot imagine that in all this you have any other aim than the desire of pleasing me; and when I see your modest blush, when your eyes meet mine, when you steal gently into my heart with soft and flattering words, I cannot, Roxana, doubt of your love.

But what am I to think of the women of Europe? The art with which they make up their complexions, the ornaments with which they bedeck themselves, the attention they pay to their person, the perpetual desire of pleasing which engrosses them, are so many stains on their virtue and outrages on their husbands.

It is not, Roxana, that I believe they push their contempt for propriety as far as such conduct would lead one to believe, and that their debauchery attains that horrible excess, at the mention of which I shudder, the absolute violation of the conjugal tie. There are few women so abandoned as to carry crime to that extent: they all bear in their souls a certain impress of virtue which has been engraved thereon at their birth, and which education weakens, but does not destroy. They may be lax enough as to the external duties which modesty exacts. When it comes to taking the final step, nature revolts; so that, when we imprison you so strictly, when we have you guarded by so many slaves, when we curb your desires with such severity, if they happen to stray beyond bounds, it is not because we dread unfaithfulness,—it is because we know that purity cannot be too stainless, and that the slightest blemish may corrupt it.

I pity you, Roxana. Your long-tried chastity merited a husband who would have never left you, and who could himself have repressed those desires which only your own virtue can now restrain.

Paris, the 7th of the moon of Rhegeb, 1712.

Among Europeans, the first quarter of an hour after marriage smoothes all difficulties. The last favors are always contemporary with the nuptial benediction; the women here are not like the women of Persia, who dispute the ground for several months; they surrender on the spot; and, if they lose nothing, it is because they have nothing to lose. But, O shameful thing! the moment of their defeat is always known, and without consulting the stars, it is always possible to predict the exact hour of their children's birth.

The French never speak of their wives; the reason is, they are afraid to speak about them before persons who are better acquainted with them than they are themselves.

There are amongst them certain very unfortunate individuals whom nobody thinks of consoling: these are the jealous husbands,—persons whom every one hates; persons whom all men scorn.

Consequently, there is no country in the world where the number of jealous husbands is so small as in France. Their tranquillity is not based on the confidence they have in their wives; it is, on the contrary, based on the ill opinion they have of them. All the wise precautions of the Asiatics,—the veils wherewith they are covered, the prisons in which they are confined, the eunuchs who watch over them, —appear to them means better calculated to exercise than to weary the astuteness of the sex. Here husbands accept their appointed destiny with a good grace, and regard the infidelities of their wives as mishaps decreed by the higher powers. A husband who wished to possess his wife to the exclusion of everybody else would be considered a disturber of the public happiness, a madman, who desired to deprive others of the light of the sun that he might enjoy it alone.

Here, if a husband loves his wife, it is a proof that he has not sufficient merit to win the love of another woman; who abuses the power given him by the law to supply those pleasures he cannot otherwise obtain; who avails himself of all his advantages to the prejudice of society at large; who appropriates to his own use what has been only given him as a pledge, and who does everything in his power to upset a tacit convention essential to the happiness of both sexes. The reputation of having a handsome wife, which is so carefully concealed in

Asia, is borne here without any anxiety: there is always the satisfaction of being able to make an attack in some other quarter. A prince consoles himself for the loss of one fortress by the capture of another. When the Turks took Baghdad from us, did not we in turn take Candaher from the Mogul?

As a rule, the man who bears patiently the infidelities of his wife is not regarded with disapproval; on the contrary, he is praised for his prudence; only in certain peculiar cases is he felt to have incurred any reproach.

It is not that there are no virtuous women; there are, and they are persons of much distinction also; my friendly guide always pointed them out to me; but they were all so ugly that one would have to be a saint not to hate virtue.

After all I have told you about the morals of this country, you can easily imagine the French do not pride themselves on their constancy: they believe that it is as ridiculous to swear eternal devotion to a woman, as it is to insist that health and happiness are going to last forever. When they promise a woman that they will always love her, they do so with the proviso that she must be always lovable; and, if she breaks her word, they do not think they are bound to keep theirs. Paris, the 7th of the moon of Zilcade, 1714.

ZELUS TO USBEK

AT PARIS

Never has a passion been more violent and impetuous than that of the Eunuch Cosrou for my slave Zelida. He asks her in marriage with such ardor that I cannot refuse him. And why should I object when her mother does not, and even Zelida herself appears to be satisfied with this delusive connection, and with the empty shadow of reality that is offered her?

Excepting, of course, that a truly loving man can probably, always find a way.

RICA TO RHEDI

AT VENICE

There are many trades, my dear Rhedi, in Paris.

There are skilful women who turn virginity into a flower that withers and is revived every day, and is gathered for the hundredth time more painfully than at first.

There are others who repair, by the excellence of their art, all the ravages of time, can restore to a face a beauty that is passing away, and can make a woman descend from the summit of old age to the freshness of youth.

All these people live, or try to live, in a city which is the mother of invention. . . .

It would be as easy to number the sands of the sea or the slaves of our monarch as to reckon up the lawyers who live upon the revenues of some mosque or other.

A countless multitude of professors of languages, arts, and sciences teach what they do not know; and their talent is not to be despised: for it requires much less wit to tell what a person knows than to teach what he is ignorant of.

It is impossible to die here, except suddenly; death has no other way of exercising his authority, because in every corner there are people who have infallible remedies for all imaginable diseases.

All the shops are provided with invisible nets in which the customers are caught; sometimes, however, a person manages to escape from them cheaply. A young saleswoman will coax a man a whole hour in order to get him to buy a package of toothpicks.

You will hardly find anyone who does not leave this city a wiser man than when he entered it. By dint of lavishing his money on others, he at last learns to keep a tight hold of it. It is the only advantage foreigners have in this bewitching city.

Most legislators here are men of limited intellect, owing their elevated position to accident, and, in almost every case, guided only by their prejudices and fancies.

Paris, the 10th of the moon of Saphar, 1714.

Incidentally, Usbek, during his long absence from Persia, has always trusted his favorite wife, Roxana, but has been deeply suspicious of one of his lesser wives, called Zachi. After a time, reports from his chief eunuch have so deeply alarmed him that

he finally gives orders to this neuter to summarily punish Zachi.
Here is the last letter from the eunuch, whose name is Solim.

SOLIM TO USBEK

AT PARIS

. . .

I swear to you by all the prophets of Heaven that, ever since you confided your wives to my care, I have watched over them night and day, and that my anxiety in their regard has never been a moment at rest. I initiated my ministry by punishments; and I suspended them without my natural austerity being affected by the change.

But what am I saying? Why do I boast of a fidelity that has been useless? Forget all my past services; look upon me as a traitor, and punish me for all the crimes I have been unable to prevent.

Roxana, the imperious Roxana—O Heaven! whom shall we henceforth trust? You suspected Zachi, but you had the utmost trust in Roxana; yet her inexorable virtue was a cruel imposture; it was the mask of perfidy. I have surprised her in the arms of a young man, who, as soon as he saw he was discovered, attacked me and struck me twice with a dagger. The eunuchs ran up, when they heard the noise, and surrounded him; he defended himself long, and wounded several of them; he then tried to return to her chamber to die, he said, beneath the eyes of Roxana. But at length he was overpowered by numbers, and fell at our feet.

I do not know, sublime lord, whether I ought to await your rigorous commands. You have placed the work of vengeance in my hands, and I ought not to let it languish.

The Seraglio at Ispahan, the 8th of the moon of Rebiab I, 1720.

ROXANA, THE FAVORITE WIFE, TO USBEK

Yes, I have deceived you; I seduced your eunuchs, made sport of your jealousy, and turned your horrible seraglio into an abode of pleasure and delight.

I am about to die; the poison is coursing through my veins. Why should I stay here when the only man who bound me to life is no more? I am dying; but my spirit flits from its mortal home splendidly attended; I have just sent before me those sacrilegious guardians who have spilt the finest blood in the world.

How could you ever have imagined that I could be so credulous as to believe I was stationed on this earth to worship your caprices, and that, while everything was permitted to yourself, you had the right to curb my desires? No! Though I have lived in servitude I have always been free. I have modified your laws in harmony with those of nature, and my spirit has ever been disenthralled.

Yet you ought to be grateful for the sacrifice I have made in lowering myself to appear faithful to you; in having cravenly held within my heart that which I should have proclaimed to the whole world, and finally, in profaning virtue in allowing my submission to your fancies to be decked with that name.

You were astonished that you did not find in me the transports of love; had you known me well, you would have found instead all the violence of hate.

But you had long the advantage of believing that a heart like mine was meekly submissive to you; we were both happy: you thought I was deceived, and it was I who deceived you.

My language, doubtless, appears strange to you. Do you think it is in my power to force you to admire my courage, even after I have crushed you with anguish? But it is nearly over, the poison consumes me; my strength is leaving me; the pen falls from my hand; even my hatred grows weak; I am dying.
The Seraglio at Ispahan, the 8th of the moon of Rebiab I, 1720.

I'm afraid I cannot conclude this section without presenting you with an actual tombstone inscription, which had originally been copied by the great short-story writer, A. E. Coppard. I found it in his autobiography, entitled *It's Me, O Lord!* I hope it will give you the same lift that I derived from the reading of it.

Between the Remains of her Brother EDWARD
   And of her Husband ARTHUR
Here lies the Body of BRIDGETT APPLEWHAIT
   Once BRIDGETT NELSON

After the Fatigues of a Married Life
Born by her with Incredible Patience
For four Years and three Quarters bating three Weeks
And after the Enjoiment of the Glorious freedom
Of an Easy and Unblemisht Widowhood
For four Years and Upwards
She Resolved to run the Risk of a Second Marriage-Bed
But DEATH forbad the Banns
And having with an Apoplectick Dart
(The same Instrument with which he had Formerly
Dispatcht her Mother)
Toucht the most Vital part of her Brain
She must have fallen Directly to the Ground
(as one Thunder-strook)
If she had not been Catcht and Supported
by her Intended Husband
Of which Invisible Bruise
After a Struggle for above Sixty Hours
With that Grand Enemy to Life
(But the certain and Merciful Friend to Helpless Old Age)
in terrible Convulsions Plaintive Groans or Stupefying Sleep
without recovery of her Speech or Senses

She dyed on the 12th day of Sep'm in ye year *of our Lord 1737*
                                                      and
                                               of her own age 44

CHAPTER TWENTY

W̲HEN I FIRST arrived in the United States I attended an ungraded class in one of the public grammar schools in
New York City.

An *ungraded* class meant that the students of that section had
only one thing in common, namely, not a single one of them
could speak much English. That room was presided over by a
middle-aged saint called Elaine Kantanogy, and some of the boys
she had to deal with were already sixteen years old, and at least
one of them, a Sicilian bandit called Amadei, had a mustache that
he used to keep properly groomed with ordinary shoe polish.
Once when Miss Kantanogy had complimented him on some
minute scholastic accomplishment he impulsively kissed her on
the cheek, and she couldn't get that black smear off her face for
the rest of the day.

At any rate, there we were, twenty-eight of us greenhorns,

stewing away over our English lesson, and all I can tell you is it was pure, unadulterated hell.

You see, those damned books that they'd dished out to us contained the weirdest goulash of tripe that anyone could possibly imagine. For instance, one of the earliest poems I had to wrestle with was a patriotic little Scottish ditty concocted by Robert Burns, and it went like this:

> *Scots, wha hae wi' Wallace bled,*
> *Scots, wham Bruce has aften led;*
> *Welcome to your gory bed,*
> *Or to victorie!*

"Well," I thought to myself, "one thing is certain, I'm never going to learn this damned language of theirs, that's for sure."

Another poem we had to memorize—or, at least, we were *expected* to learn it by heart—was Gray's "Elegy Written in a Country Churchyard." I think it had somewhere around twenty stanzas and an epitaph. The poem starts with this:

> *The curfew tolls the knell of parting day,*
> *The lowing herd winds slowly o'er the lea,*
> *The plowman homeward plods his weary way,*
> *And leaves the world to darkness and to me.*

After a while I did get some satisfaction out of the fact that no student attending that school had the vaguest idea what any of this meant. Even boys in the graduating class couldn't tell me what *curfew* or *knell* or *lea* signified, and I finally settled down to the conviction that this was a country in which several languages were being spoken simultaneously and that I'd just have to learn the one that seemed to be the most popular.

You probably can't help wondering what sort of numskull had introduced such books into the school system, but the truth is I found equally senseless ones later on in the higher grades and my children, who acquired their education some decades afterward, were confronted by texts which were just as unsuitable and also totally idiotic. At the very least, they were unbelievably boring, and I can assure you that their hatred of Walter Scott dates right back to their earliest childhood.

Before you start pitying us, I advise you to take a good look at some of the dreary material that is being used in textbooks nowadays, and you will come to realize that the boneheads who make the critical decisions about such things are as far out of touch with reality as they ever were.

The wonder is that anyone ever survives these ordeals and sometimes, despite all of his bewilderment, even manages to acquire a taste for serious reading. Of course, I'd had my good break back in Austria, so I just went on borrowing books from the Ottendorfer branch of the public library, down on Eighth Street and Second Avenue, because in that delightfully old-fashioned little building they carried a vast supply of all of the best German literature.

In recent years I also bought a good many scientific books— everything from astronomy to zoology—and my wife and I often read aloud to one another about the endlessly fascinating miracles of our universe.

You'd be surprised how much you can learn by giving some really concentrated attention to these seemingly difficult subjects. Happily, during recent years, a good many distinguished scholars have learned to communicate with people who are neither specialists nor just nincompoops who like to collect a lot of odd facts with which to astonish the girls around the office water cooler.

Well, a few months ago, when my wife's birthday happened to roll around again, I suddenly decided to buy her a telescope. This wasn't such an unusual idea as you might think, when you consider that she cares very little for jewelry and she certainly isn't interested in owning any fur coats. At any rate, I ordered this instrument, a really good-sized apparatus, and when it arrived it turned out to be a smash success.

Naturally, we had to have some expert advice on putting it into working order, and the people who had sold it to me sent around a pleasant and knowledgeable person who gave us a thorough rundown on the basic essentials. Of course, a telescope doesn't make much sense in a city apartment, but we were planning to make extensive use of it later on, after we got out into the country; but by the time we were ready to leave for Connecticut both of us had managed to forget the meatiest parts of those pretty complicated instructions. I didn't want to bother the optical people a second time, so I called a friend of mine who has quite a few acquaintances in stargazing circles and he recommended a man called Harold Ramey, who specialized in setting up all sorts of astronomical paraphernalia.

Ramey showed up at my home a couple of days before we were ready to start off, and in no time at all he had everything shipshape.

Now then, you must remember that, in the last five years, I've become known to a vast number of people, and it seems that a majority of these creatures fancy themselves to be absolutely enthralling raconteurs. You know the type, that just tells one bum joke after another, and he generally endorses these verbal cripples by assuring you that you are free to use this comic material of his either in your books or even on TV, since there is plenty more left where this great stuff all came from.

I find that most of this humor is derived out of comic almanacs, but I've noticed that the more up-to-date scavengers simply crib their stuff out of the *Reader's Digest*. In any event, I want you to know that I'm the daily victim of these depressing regurgitations, since hardly a waiter or taxi driver in Greater New York ever misses the chance to enrich my life with just such rancid dribblings.

So, after Mr. Ramey had set up the telescope in my living room, I heard with a sinking heart that he was giving a few socially preparational coughs, which, in my sad experience, generally presage the imminent delivery of some humdinger of a joke that is sure to make me sick for a couple of hours at the very least.

"These are very fine instruments," he said. "Quite a few people are buying them nowadays."

"I'm glad to hear that," I said, eyeing him rather uneasily, because he still had that special smirk on his face, which, with amateur entertainers, indicates that they're so full of laughs they can barely manage to contain themselves.

"Yeah," he said. "Shelley Winters just bought one just like this."

"That's fine," I said, bracing myself for a crack about a *star* who spends her time *stargazing*. Get it?

But nothing of the sort happened. Mr. Ramey just leaned up against my doorpost and slowly started to talk. I think he was talking more to himself than to me, because after a while I could hardly manage to hear him. It was more like a barely audible, ruminative research into his past, and the substance of what he came up with was this:

"About six months ago a man named Stanley Bowker called me on the telephone and asked me to set up an instrument like this in his home. Well, I went up there around six o'clock one evening, and there is this very nervous-looking feller and he's really not paying the slightest attention to my instructions. So I told him to make himself some notes, because it isn't really that simple, but he just waved me off and told me to set the telescope right up against the window. I said to him, 'There isn't much sense in setting it up against the window, because the house across the way completely blocks out the sky.'

" 'Never mind about *that*,' he said. 'I just want to get the eighth floor on the other side. I want that corner apartment, the one with the blue drapes—see what I mean?'

" 'Well,' I said, 'you could have just bought yourself a pair of binoculars for that purpose; you didn't really need such a complicated telescope.'

" 'That's what *you* think,' he said. 'I've got *two* pairs of binoculars, and I'm getting nowhere *fast* with both of them right now.'

" 'I suppose you know best where you want to *get*,' I said.

" 'That's right,' he said. 'You know what goes on in that corner room over there? Every single night of the week a woman comes home and, after she gets completely undressed, she takes a bass fiddle out of a closet and starts practicing right near that last window. Did you ever *see* or *hear* a woman bass fiddler in all of your life?'

" 'No,' I said, 'I never have.'

" 'Well, neither has anybody else. Tell me something—how much does that telescope enlarge a person's vision?'

" 'About three hundred times,' I said.

" 'Great! Well, let me tell *you* something, mister: I'm going to get to the bottom of this damned thing *if it takes me all winter!*' "

CHAPTER TWENTY-ONE

In the mid-twenties the Sirfessor Klondike developed some serious liver condition and was carted off to Bellevue Hospital.

He had a room all to himself, which is always a bad sign with a charity patient, and as I sat by his bedside I couldn't help wondering what sort of thoughts were passing through his mind as he lay there in that ghastly building with sick and dying strangers groaning and screaming in the cubicles all around him.

"Tell me," I said, "after you get out of here, do you plan to change your life in any way at all?"

"It is a most flattering idea that you think I *might*," he said. "But, actually, a man has very little choice about such things. Don't you see—once you've reached your thirties, your habits have completely established themselves and it is *they* that make all the important decisions for you and all that is left for you to do is to justify what you are no longer able to alter. I daresay I could have had another sort of existence altogether. Who knows? With a little good fortune I might have become seriously ill quite a few years ago and, out of a sheer blind instinct to preserve myself, I might perhaps even have developed a real distaste for liquor. It certainly is too late now. It is nearly always too late for people who are deficient in nervous energy. They are destined to go relentlessly downhill, because at one time or another they are bound to settle for much too little."

"Sirfessor," I said, "do *you* believe that there *is* a life after birth?"

"Only for the very lucky few," he said. "The rest are condemned to muff the whole deal, because they can't help treating this precious gift as if it were only a sum of money. I suppose it is shrewd to invest your ready capital for a quick return. But to invest your life on the same terms is certain to defraud you out of the whole works. You see, there is nothing a man can ever come to value which has accrued to him too easily and without any real effort. It is like a law in physics. No action—no *re*action. The knowledge that is stored in our great books, the exquisite perfections of art, the incredible wonder and mystery inherent in all of nature require that a man apply himself lovingly to their deciphering. So, if we want a lot of fast action and a quick payoff, we are doomed to wind up with just a stack of worthless chips. What is more, I think everything is going to get a great deal worse and, as far as I can guess, things are not ever likely to get better again either."

The nurse came into the room at this point to take his temperature and his blood pressure, and after she had gone he said, "Can you possibly imagine what will finally become of all those charts and graphs which have accumulated in this building throughout the years? The doctors who call on me every morning have to look at several hundred patients every day, so naturally they can't be bothered to read up on all the fluctuating circulatory calamities which are checked off here every three hours. In short, they are collecting all this data merely to keep their files in good shape and all of this tabulating activity has actually no real connection with any of the human beings involved in it. I think that this in itself is a symptom of a very desperate social illness, which is a thousand times more alarming than any arterial disasters that only threaten the lives of a few elderly people. However, let me proceed with more important matters. For instance, let us take a look at a man like Thomas Jefferson, who was probably one of the greatest souls who ever inhabited this foolish globe. Jefferson lived and died in the belief that this country was destined to be ruled by an exalted aristocracy of the spirit. It was a noble consolation to a man who didn't really believe in very much else. At any rate, he couldn't possibly foresee the industrial revolution, and that after a time some pretty tenacious shrewdies, who were also more than ordinarily ruthless, might come to achieve almost complete mastery over a great many other human destinies. He functioned in a sparsely populated, largely agricultural country, and it would never have occurred to him that inside this ideal republic there might emerge the Kingdom of Steel, the Kingdom of Oil, the Kingdom of Aluminum and even the Kingdom of Coca-Cola. Even so, I suppose he would have argued that the groundwork had been laid to keep the worst scoundrels in check, and that for the first time in history, mankind was in control of a social mechanism that could serve as an effective tool to bring the greatest good to the greatest number, unless the majority voluntarily gave up all of its basic rights."

"Well, that certainly hasn't happened," I said.

"No, I suppose not," he admitted. "But, what *has* happened is something equally disastrous. The majority no longer bothers to pay even lip service to the aristocracy of the spirit. It has, instead, set up the idols of ostentatious material success in all the high places of the republic, and it kowtows to these shimmering effigies exactly as the ancient worshipers of the ox-headed Baal used to bow down to *their* pre-Christian idols. To be a truly learned man surely meant something in the time of Jefferson. Nowadays it only means that you are never likely to make yourself a really sizable pile of lucre. Hardly anyone goes to school because he wants his mind and his spirit to be enlarged; he just wants to get some kind of a degree that will enable him to get a fat job or earn a successful promotion. I think that if things continue as they are going along at this time, every single inhabitant of this entire country will eventually wind up with a college diploma. It may very well be that we will become the first nation of academically certified ignoramuses extant in the whole world. I also believe that a good many people are thoroughly convinced that this, indeed, is the true meaning of *Democracy in Action*. Now then, after every living moron in the land has achieved at least a bachelor of arts degree, nobody will have the right to look *down* on him, but, what is even more important, *he* won't have to look *up* to anybody *either*. Well, thank heaven, I won't live to see all this revolting business in its final apotheosis of confusion. And as far as your question is concerned—of whether there *is* a life after birth—I can only repeat what I said to you before: it just depends on your luck, I suppose. Not everyone has the good fortune to be endowed with a lively imagination, and very few people ever manage to achieve an even halfway satisfactory state of awareness. Most of us just vegetate along from day to day as so many narcotically addicted Hopers and Expecters, although there surely isn't any logical reason why we should anticipate anything, excepting just a great big hang-up. Frankly, I think life is mostly just a dirty trick, with some short interludes of Coney Island popcorn thrown in. So, you see, I'm not in the least bit disillusioned. I think there *is* a life after birth, provided that all of the seven good fairies happen to be present at your emergence out of the womb. I can tell you, for myself, that only *six* of those dear creatures made their appearance at my debut, and so I never really felt quite alive unless I was able to eke out this deficiency with some secondhand magic, like booze."

A couple of weeks after we'd had this talk, about half a dozen of my friends chipped in with me to have the Sirfessor cremated. When I went up to the undertaking parlor to make the necessary arrangements, a strange man turned up in the lobby of the mortuary establishment and told me that he was the brother of the deceased. He was a tall, scrawny, red-nosed individual who hadn't

shaved for quite a while, and when I asked him to identify himself a little more circumstantially, he said, "I'm a Sofessor meself.
Fact is, I wuz a Sofessor five years afore him. I don't want nuthin'
fum him, I just come to claim his overcoat an' his briefcase; on
account of I lent dem to him a long time ago, an' he never brung
'em back."

"That overcoat is all split open on one side," I said. "And the
briefcase has no flap and the lock is torn off."

"It don' madder ta me," said the stranger. "Sediment is sediment, an' besides, he wuz my own flesh an' blood, weren't he?"

"I haven't the vaguest idea," I said. "One thing I'm sure of,
though, old Klondike would certainly like for you to have his belongings. In fact, I've got a feeling he's laughing his head off right
now, wherever the hell he is."

"I don' tink dis is de time for swearin'," said the suddenly
purse-mouthed heir, as I handed him the dingy parcel containing
the Sirfessor's total earthly estate.

CHAPTER TWENTY-TWO

In late january 1959, my first book, called *Mine Enemy Grows Older*, started to sell into the several thousands each week. It was a real phenomenon, since it was an autobiography by a completely obscure human being and, what is more, it didn't have any dirty stories in it.

I'll try to give you an idea how it all happened. I had begun the writing of this book about two and a half years before, and when I finally managed to get together one hundred and eighty-four pages, I gave my manuscript to my old friend Albert Hirschfeld, who is so close to me that I knew if he thought badly of my efforts he would never trouble to butter me up about it.

Albert read my stuff very carefully, and I can't tell you how pleased I was when he told me that he liked it.

"I think we ought to let Sid Perelman read it," he said. "After all, he's a friend of yours, too, and maybe he'll make some helpful suggestions."

And that's exactly what we did.

Sid, who was a neighbor of mine down in Greenwich Village at that time, called me on the phone and expressed himself very enthusiastically about the book and even suggested that it might be a good idea if he submitted my fragmentary manuscript to his publishers, Simon and Schuster.

I just want you to know that among real professionals there is no jealousy and there is always a great deal of disinterested maneuvering to bring a decent piece of work to the attention of the proper people.

Later on I will tell you a little something about Alexander Woollcott and Frank Crowninshield, who, more than thirty years ago, also exerted themselves most generously in my behalf.

But back to Simon and Schuster. They liked my promise of a book well enough to give me a small advance, and by the spring of 1958 I delivered the finished job at their offices. My treasured epic was scheduled in their November catalogue and I was fortunate enough to receive so much favorable advance comment from various influential sources that for the first time in my life I permitted myself to indulge in rather optimistic fancies about a project that carried my name.

Well, the book finally appeared and was, by and large, received rather indulgently by the country's press, and in two or three particularly meaningful metropolitan reviews, I even managed to garner some outright praise.

So far, so good.

And then, suddenly, a fat load of pure disaster fell right down on top of me. You see, the truck drivers who distribute the newspapers in New York City decided to go out on strike just before Christmas, which means that although I had gotten very good reviews, nobody had a chance to read them.

At any rate, the book didn't go any too well, and you can just imagine my despair.

It seemed to me that I had been a great fool to think that anyone would give a damn about an autobiography written by a comparative nonentity, no matter how wittily or sincerely the job might have been done. That is to say, all the pros in the publishing and theatrical world were familiar enough with my name, but most of the individuals in these professions quite naturally expected to get my book for nothing, suitably inscribed to them, of course.

So I ran frantically up to Simon and Schuster in the hope that some particularly inspired individual at this firm would be able to think of an emergency measure that might help to rescue my masterpiece from seemingly inevitable oblivion.

To tell you the truth, nobody was very optimistic about my chances. They'd managed to unload about five thousand copies of the book (which covered their expenses as well as my advance), and, by and large, they had pretty well decided that in the meanwhile they had all better concentrate on the salability of some of their *other* books.

As a matter of fact, the original picture for my cover jacket, which I had painted myself, was still standing up against the wall in some guy's office at the time, and the white-collar worker who occupied that cubicle made it pretty plain to me that this piece of artwork was seriously obstructing traffic around the place.

It was a hell of a mess.

And then somebody suggested that it might be a good idea if I went on a couple of radio programs and tried to peddle my stuff to the public directly. A few authors had already done this, with mixed or even doubtful results, but I certainly was eager to try it —no matter how questionable the outcome.

The first program I appeared on was a radio broadcast that took place early Saturday mornings, and when I arrived at the studio the place was jammed with footloose, bewinged airplane hostesses and several troops of colored Boy Scouts. What's more, everybody was munching chocolate-covered breakfast cereal, which the sponsor had freely showered all over this semiconscious audience.

I was shattered, of course, and when a drooling elderly idiot in that crowd of numskulls showed me a dozen admission tickets that he had managed to nail for other broadcasts, I just told him to go and fall in the crapper. That audience simply got me down. There obviously weren't any book buyers among these people, and I was sure that most of them probably had great difficulty in deciphering even the large print on their comic books.

The man who ran that unbelievable program was one of those gravel-voiced, homespun types that absolutely give me the willies. He told jokes out of some old Joe Miller comic albums, and all I remember is that by the time it was my turn to join him on the podium I was so nauseated I had to hold a protective handkerchief in front of my face.

Somebody had typed some wisecracks out of my book onto a sheet of paper, and although the chief gazabo, or whatever the hell he was, had the volume itself right on the table, I was convinced that this oaf had never bothered to read even the publisher's blurb on the outside.

He beamed at me, of course, and said, "Well, how do *you* feel this fine morning, Mr. King?"

"I feel like a prematurely born fetus," I said. "I've been listening to you for the past half hour—and I can honestly say that I've never before in all my life been immersed so derrière-deep in wholesomeness."

I really don't know whether anyone in that unfortunate gathering had the vaguest idea what I was talking about—all I can tell you is that they gave me a great big hand. This unexpected applause heartened me sufficiently to take complete charge. I ignored the questions of my interlocutor from then on and just proceeded to tell a couple of the briefer ancedotes out of my book. The time passed quickly enough, and when it was all over, several of the people on my benefactor's staff came around to congratulate me.

"You were a wonderful guest," one of them said to me. "You ought to go on TV. You ought to go on the 'Jack Paar Show.' I think you'd be very good, and he'd like you."

Well, I'm not going to torture you with any minute recital of what happened to me in the next few weeks. Suffice it to say that I appeared on eleven different radio and TV shows and the results, as far as my book sales were concerned, were almost negligible.

But, finally, I did make the "Jack Paar Show," which was broadcast in those days *live* from the old Hudson Theater. The first time I was on I didn't make my appearance until about ten minutes of one, which meant that I had only about four minutes on the air.

I was sweating with anxiety, of course. I realized that I had to *do* or *say* something really startling if I expected to make any sort of impact on the listening audience. Fortunately, I'd had a letter that very morning from a dear book critic from some Southern paper, a man totally unknown to me, who had loved my work and deeply sympathized with me for my multifarious physical ailments.

Among other things, he had written me the following: "I understand you have only a small fraction of one kidney left. I heard, or read, recently somewhere, that kidney transplants from one person to another have become feasible lately, and if this is really so, then please feel free to call on me. I have two sound kidneys, and you are welcome to have one of them. I would not, offhand, guarantee the soundness of any of my other organs *that come in pairs*, but I am quite sure that my kidneys are altogether normal and healthy."

Well, I quoted this letter verbatim on that first Jack Paar program, and all I can tell you is that that studio audience laughed for a full minute and a half.

I was in.

I was in in more ways than one, since my publisher received orders for twenty-eight thousand books in the next six days. That first volume of my autobiography eventually sold over two million copies in the hard-cover and paperback releases.

My second volume outsold the first in hard covers.

The third one was on the best-seller lists for nearly twenty weeks and did very well in the cheaper-priced edition also.

I have, in the past three years, appeared almost two hundred times on TV and radio, and that original book-jacket drawing of mine that was in everybody's way when my book wasn't selling was exhibited in many bookshop windows all over the country.

During the last four years about a hundred authors have peddled their products on the "Jack Paar Show," and only Jack's own book managed to sell anywhere near as well as mine. Which only goes to prove that there is, after all, no surefire road to success, even if you do get exactly the same chances as the guys who somehow, mysteriously, made it.

The real irony of the whole matter lies, of course, in the fact that I loathe most of TV and think that as an entertainment medium it is beneath criticism.

I'm very grateful, just the same.

In connection with my belated literary success, I want to tell you about the numerous people who have written to me, asking for advice about their own writing efforts. I had letters from retired mail carriers and ex-garage men who were in the mood for making a few additional dollars by going into the writing game. The belief that this can actually be done is one of the many American folk superstitions which absolutely fracture me. Whenever I see an advertisement that encourages people to try for some easy bucks in the literary marketplace I get deeply depressed. I often feel like buying some space in the same papers just to tell all these poor misguided schnooks to *lay off*. I want to say, *"Kids, you're being had. Somebody is out to gyp you. There ain't no such thing as an easy dollar in them there ditches. You're only wasting your hard-earned dough!"*

The reason I don't do it is because I know damned well that these benighted suckers aren't going to believe me anyway. Besides, maybe it gives them some pleasure to mail out their hopekites, and to get them back from the big city with all those interesting rejection slips attached to their tails.

Some of my correspondents have taken my earnest candor with a good deal of ill feeling. They point out that I myself was fifty-eight years old before I finally managed to ring the bell.

Horse manure, fellers! All just a lot of horse manure!

My first written efforts were published when I was fifteen. I worked on newspapers as a writer-illustrator when I was seventeen. I wrote for *Smart Set*, for *Vanity Fair*, for *Vogue*, for *The New Yorker*, and I even made a very good living for quite a number of years as a play doctor. So, don't give me that stuff that you're never too old to try. *I don't believe any part of that nonsense.* Anybody who has been tending bar or waiting at tables all his life is never going to be a writer. You can take my word for *that.*

As for ideas—well, I know at least fifty people who earn their keep by their varying literary skills, and I never heard of a single one among them who was looking for other people's ideas. Ideas are cheaper than dirt. I myself always have a couple of hundred to spare on any subject from adultery to xenophobia, and I know they won't do anybody else a damned bit of good.

In fact, the only place where ideas could be sold for cash was in Hollywood in the silly old days, and that's exactly why the movie companies finally took such a nose dive.

My great cry throughout the years has consistently been *"Please don't give me any ideas! I've got more than I can handle right now!"*

Believe me, for a professional writer one lifetime isn't long enough just to put down even a small fraction of the notions that keep passing through his head all of the time.

That's a trade secret I'm letting you in on for nothing.

So, if you're over fifty years old and you've sold a story to the Williford *Bugle* about the last veterans' reunion, and even if you got ten dollars' worth of S & H stamps for it, I beg you with all my heart, don't bother writing me about it. *And I especially beg of you not to send me any plots on the earnings of which we're supposed to go halvies.*

By the way, I mentioned Woollcott and Crowninshield a little while back, and I'd like to pay my respects to these good men before I get all balled up in something else.

Woollcott was once the drama critic on the New York *World*, one of the finest newspapers ever published in this country. I worked for him for quite a few years, and in due time he became my very dear friend. He lent me money, he put me up at his home, he got me jobs, and he advised me on all occasions when it looked like I might be heading for a collision.

Crowninshield was editor of the best magazine ever printed in the United States, and Crownie lent me money, put me up at his home, got me a lot of jobs, and advised me on many matters pertaining to my career and even on some rather minutely delicate points connected with my purely personal affairs.

I remember them both with deep gratitude and affection. They were that rarest of all things in this world, they were people one could actually turn to when one needed any sort of help.

In 1932 I owned and edited a satirical magazine called *Americana*, and in one of its issues I printed a piece called "This Is Woollcott Speaking." He used to give a weekly radio broadcast at that time, and for the benefit of my readers I decided to do a short verbal sketch of him. Here is that piece I wrote over thirty years ago:

His window frames the soiled slow motion of the East River. A fortuitous accident has located a huge dynamo just a few blocks from his dwelling, and the fine, almost imperceptible vibration generated by this monster gives the alert visitor the sensation of being at sea.

His cabin is sedately furnished with the mementos of past or transient exuberances. He lies or lolls amidst his cozy treasures in a decent state of undress and serves refreshments to visiting passengers from bottles that bear the crest of Great Catherine.

His enormous body occasionally shrinks and sometimes entirely disappears as if the whole huge torso were at the command of his carefully poised wit. He is the extrabiological offspring of Charles Dickens and Jean Cocteau, a baffling combination of Victorian sentimentality and French esprit. The Cheeryble Brothers were his godfathers, and there can be no doubt that Humpty Dumpty made the usually appropriate remarks at his christening.

He loves the theater and its puppets, and despite his profound cynicism toward actors and a penetrating eye for their paltry machinations he has become the plump and jovial pontiff for hundreds of stage people. He loves all talent and is most injudiciously extreme in his enthusiasm for trivial accomplishments. He gossips like a fishwife but seasons the poisonous accuracy of his estimates with eulogistic asides which frequently transform his aspersions into devious, extravagant praise.

The territory of his body is too large for his overseeing, and it is natural to find the cord of his dressing gown hanging from his neck like a slain snake, or some remnant of sweetmeat gently melting in the folds of his chin. His innocence beguiles the wary, and he has some subtle psychic advantage by telling the truth more often than is commonly the custom. He has invented himself and his role. Without the appearance of eccentricity he has become unique as a raconteur, host, globe-trotter and journalist.

On some trifling pretext I paid him a visit to verify the circumstances of his preparation for an impending radio broadcast. I stepped into the semidarkness of his cabin and he received me affably and without preoccupation. I knew that within the next hour he was to speak into a microphone, and it was my psychopathic privilege to feel the nervousness which logically enough should have been his. Perhaps he was uneasy. There was no way of telling, since he spoke with ease and fluency upon the subject which had furnished the reason for my calling.

His room hummed as usual. The ghosts of his departed guests still troubled the uneasy air. I knew them all, by sight, sound or reputation: the young millionaire Communist who wore his unshaven face and flannel shirt like a uniform; the witty newspaperwoman who, with an ingenue lisp, annihilated continents; the charming actress, to whom all rooms were stage sets.

Why did they come to him? Why did I come? Probably because he is clever. Because, despite all dull and ponderous detractors, cleverness is rare as wisdom. Because of six people whom one was likely to meet in his cabin, at least two would be amusing and the other four would understand and appreciate this astonishing and delightful circumstance.

In the spotlight of the bridge lamp, his stomach, like a giant gourd, rumbled with sinister fermentations. I sometimes puzzle about this formidable protuberance. Has he dragged it all through the war? Is it a later acquisition? Is it perhaps the storehouse for his gaseous effronteries?

He has made himself a crusader against "Whimsy." Is he aware how close he comes to being whimsical and how often he is prettily precious in his tastes? Is it a defense mechanism?

He writes well. He is an excellent journalist. He has the good, keen eye of the true newspaperman. This seemingly indolent man produces enormous quantities of bright, systematic work. He is feminine in his perceptions but brusque beyond the daring of the most intrepid dowager. He speaks with the casual mastery of the born raconteur who knows that the ends of his sentences will take care of themselves.

At last he rises and, assuming his metaphorical tippet and galoshes, he ambles out into the night. At the radio station he glances once more through his material. He is given the signal to speak, and after one last furtive cigarette he recites part of The Hunting of the Snark into a faintly surprised microphone.

CHAPTER TWENTY-THREE

I'D LIKE TO SAY just a few more words on the subject of writing. Quite a number of people have sent me letters telling me that their lives had been more than usually active, and in several instances they even gave rather fascinating examples of adventures and experiences which were certainly far from common. These correspondents all asked me whether I believed that their exciting, factual recollections might perhaps prove to be interesting reading material for the public at large.

I can only tell you what I know, and what I know is that no publisher I ever met cares to receive autobiographies from people who failed to become famous or who, at least, didn't manage to become rather picturesquely *in*famous. The only exception I can think of might be someone whose writing clearly demonstrates a great mastery of English, in which case the editors will assuredly inquire of him whether he happens to be planning any work of fiction in the near future. This pleasant contingency having been hopefully raised, they will assure him of a prompt and sympathetic reading, and the letter will then come to a close with the usual ritualistic business amenities.

Of course, if it has been your destiny to be stranded in the Australian bush, and early one morning you happened to come on a deserted clutch of platypus eggs, and after having instituted a diligent but fruitless search for the negligent mother you had resolutely decided to squat down and hatch out that brood all by yourself—well, then you've got hold of a story whose infinite sales possibilities are beyond the most optimistic conjectures.

Or let us suppose that at one time or another, in the jungles of some far-off country, you accidentally fell in with a female albino ocelot who was desperately unpopular in big-time cat circles. Let us further assume that after befriending this creature, you finally painted a lot of waterproof spots all over her, which made her socially acceptable in even the most self-consciously speckled ocelot circles. And if, later on, out of sheer gratitude, that amiable carnivore brought a few of her albino offspring to your kitchen for an allover retouching job, then it stands to reason that the book clubs will bludgeon each other to a standstill to get hold of your opus and, as far as I can see, your only trouble will be to find a place to live where the income-tax rate is more elastic than it is in this country.

You see, friends, in a world as shaky and mixed up as this one, we all like to believe that somewhere on this bedeviled globe the simple virtues can still, somehow, manage to prevail. Also, we are desperately beguiled by the notion that it is possible for someone to love us absolutely and uncritically. Idyllic situations such as these transport us automatically back into the realm of our childhood, in which every cucumber and every passing lizard was conveniently anthropomorphized in order to fit in with the playful patterns of our harmless fancies.

The popularity of such books is founded on the fact that we can at once endow these four-footed protagonists with all sorts of human attributes and we are furthermore in the happy position not to be burdened with any of their human failings. Whatever may, later on, turn out to be cruel or revolting in these creatures will have to be justly accredited to their quite naturally deep seated animal instincts.

So you can easily see that the canine or the feline or the rodent hero has an immediate advantage over any mere man. He is tender and devoted and grateful in the best sense of the Christian ethic, and if he should suddenly decide to tear off your kneecap or to pee into your fireplace he is instantly exonerated, since everyone understands his unique status as a wild, untrammeled spirit who is just desperately trying to set up his awkward contacts with the elusive ethical concepts of the YMCA.

You might as well face it, you can't beat a hero like *that*.

Here is another aspect of my mail: Quite a few of my correspondents asked me what I thought about moving pictures which purported to translate the great works of literature into the medium of the so-called silver screen.

Well, I can tell you clearly and unequivocally that this process has *never* worked. There is no such thing as a moving picture that can possibly do justice to a great book. The only thing that is sure to get lost in such an adaptation is the author's most treasured skill—his capacity as a writer.

Tolstoi, Conrad, Hemingway took a great number of years to perfect themselves in the highly exigent craft of literature, and naturally the first thing that is bound to suffer defenestration when a movie hack gets his manicured claws on any of their labors is the original writer's painfully acquired verbal technique.

So, if you've seen *War and Peace* or *An Outcast of the Islands*, you can't lay the slightest claim to having any real knowledge of what Tolstoi and Conrad had in mind when they sat down to write these fine books.

I remember reading *An Outcast of the Islands* about forty-five years ago, and I can recall the first few sentences out of that work absolutely verbatim to this very day. Since I'm writing these pages up here in Connecticut and my books are all in New York City, I don't happen to have this volume around; nevertheless, I haven't the slightest hesitation in putting down the beginning of that story, even though the basic source for a check reference is not within my reach at this moment.

Here is how it goes:

"When he stepped off the straight and narrow path of his peculiar honesty, it was with an inward assertion of unflinching resolve to fall back again into the monotonous but safe stride of virtue as soon as his little excursion into the wayside quagmires had produced its desired effect. It was going to be a short episode —a sentence in brackets, so to speak—in the flowing tale of his life: a thing to be done unwillingly, yet neatly, and to be quickly forgotten."

The reason I remember these sentences so well is because when my eyes first ran across those lines I realized with profound foreboding that nothing good could possibly come of it to the man involved. His name, I discovered later on, was Willems, and I knew that human life allowed no margins for *sentences in brackets* and that opportunistic excursions into facile crime or riskful experiments to achieve an unearned shortcut to tinselly splendor could never be just casual asides in the bitterly circumscribed life of man. I recall that when I began to read that book I felt instinctively that that small sentence in brackets was destined to destroy all of the normal habit patterns to which Willems had become acclimated over the years and that his future was now irrevocably committed to a dark and unpredictable end.

And what do I remember from the moving picture that was made of this story?

I remember Robert Morley, a competent actor, dismally miscast as the fretful Allmayer, and I vaguely recall the heroine, an Egyptian girl who didn't speak a word in any language throughout the entire length of the film and who, as far as I know, hasn't uttered a single sound in any other picture made since that time.

I'm not going to bother talking about *War and Peace* at all, because, along with millions of other literate people, I consider it to be the greatest novel ever written. The idea that a bunch of Hollywood ignoramuses were allowed to vandalize this masterpiece just indicates that my hopes for man's eventual redemption have certainly suffered a serious retardation, which, in this instance at least, may amount to a setback totaling up to several centuries.

I had just finished writing the foregoing lines when Dr. Kohler suddenly appeared in my workroom. He drops by once or twice a week just to see how I'm holding up, and I generally try, with all my ingenuity, to get rid of him as soon as possible. This afternoon, after he'd given me an examination, I was shattered to hear that someone was planning to phone him at my house and that he meant to stay here until that call came through. In my despair I planted him out on our back lawn, handed him a hunk of my typed manuscript, put a glass of iced tea on a table beside him, and dashed right back to my work.

The damned phone didn't ring for nearly half an hour, but I must confess he didn't bother me at all; and then, just before he left the house, he said, "I notice a slight oversight, a *lacuna*, in that musical sanitarium of yours. I have found that two standard types are always present in all institutions of that sort: the elderly misogynist and the permanently enraged spinster. Well, you forgot about them."

He was quite right. Every nut-hatchery that I have ever been in had those two on hand at all times.

The man is generally in his late fifties, and the last one I happened to encounter up at Dr. Moreno's clinic had a dutiful wife who paid him a visit at least once each week. This guy's vitriolic hatred of women stemmed from his firm belief that he would have been a very successful dramatist if only he hadn't married at the age of twenty-eight. He felt that his whole life had been thrown out of kilter because of his wife's eagerness to become a mother. They were childless, of course.

The standard demented spinster present on location at that particular moment of my life was so consistently and so ruggedly on the make that no man—not even any of the hospital doctors—dared to be alone with her at any time.

After I'd thought about this for a little while I decided to add a couple of stanzas to my masquerade-ball lyric which these two

standard sanitarium representatives might possibly come to sing
at one another.

ELDERLY MISOGYNIST

"Oh, it's better far to mate than sublimate"
Is the battle cry of females throughout life.
It is better far to mate than sublimate
If a maiden ever hopes to be a wife.
But the poetry and painting that one praises
And the genius that made Satsuma vases
And the seeds that sprout in cultural oases
Are of more endearing patterns
Than the unborn brats of slatterns
Who want husbands for their blind ovarian phases.

FURIOUS SPINSTER

Only selfish, all too selfish,
Like a mud-encrusted shellfish,
Your philosophy of impotence is nil.
You are merely babbling phrases,
Since the artists who made vases
All had families who carried on their skill.
They were absolutely healthy,
Quite a few of them were wealthy,
While your manner's mean and stealthy
And you're obviously ill.

CHAPTER TWENTY-FOUR

SINCE I seem to have reached a point where I'm paying my long-overdue *devoirs* to teachers, benefactors, monitors
and guides, it behooves me to recall Boruch Fleitmann, the man
who first put me on the right track to unravel the peculiar mys-
tique of the Jewish joke.

It was about the middle of 1917, when I worked for a Yiddish
humorous weekly called *The Big Stick*. I've written about that
pretty extensively in several other places, but I have never told
the story of the pale, dark-haired hunchback who used to come to
our editorial offices almost every week down on East Broadway,
to sell us jokes.

I suppose the selling of comic material of any sort isn't the
easiest way to earn a living, even under the best of circumstances,
but on a Jewish publication, where everyone, including the office
boy, considers himself a qualified expert on all matters pertaining
to humor, the situation is bound to reach absolutely grotesque

proportions. I remember the first time that Boruch Fleitmann happened to drop into the place; I was immediately struck by the almost dramatic mournfulness of his appearance and demeanor. As with most hunchbacks, his head seemed enormously oversized, and his moist black eyes, burning in deeply embedded sockets, were simply brimming over with unutterable sadness. It was obvious to me that he was an old contributor to our paper, since hardly anyone bothered to give him greetings as he entered the editorial room and quietly went over to the office samovar to pour himself a glass of tea. He drank his tea Russian-fashion, that is to say, he clamped half a lump of sugar between his enormous teeth and sipped the scalding beverage noisily through this quickly melting strainer.

After about ten minutes, Jack Marinoff, the owner-editor of *The Big Stick*, abandoned an old Warsaw gazette he had been reading and, looking distrustfully at Fleitmann over the top of his steel-rimmed glasses, said, "Noo?"

Fleitmann slowly slurped up the rest of his tea, looked speculatively at Marinoff for a moment, and said noncommittally; "Noo—noo—!"

Marinoff yawned, scratched his head, and finally, staring concentratedly out of a nearby window, said: And what sort of lousy jokes have you got for us *this* time?"

Now it was Fleitmann's turn to do some extensive yawning, and after he had elaborately scratched himself under one armpit he said in a barely audible voice: "This rich Jew went to the synagogue on Friday night and he invited a poor traveling scholar to come to his home for dinner. This rich Jew had a bad reputation for stinginess and the tired, hungry scholar was not too happy to go along with him, but since there weren't any better offers available, he finally wrapped up his prayer shawl and followed the wealthy merchant toward his nearby home. The dinner was, of course, pretty sparse, and when the main meat course was served the scholar suddenly burst into loud and bitter tears. Naturally, everyone at the table looked in great consternation at the weeping guest, and at last the head of the house inquired for the cause of all this sorrow.

" 'I'll tell you the truth,' said the scholar, wiping some stray tears from his cheeks. 'When I look at this teeny-weeny shred of beef on my plate, it just breaks my heart to think that a great big ox had to pay with his life just to produce this measly trifle.' "

Now, first of all, let's get one thing straight: this story loses about eighty-five percent of its merit by being translated into English. That can't be helped. Luckily, I had, by that time, learned enough Yiddish to get the whole gist of it without any difficulty at all, and so, when Fleitmann had finished, I laughed out loud.

Marinoff stared at me with a face showing unmistakable disgust. "This is the office of a joke paper," he said to me sternly. "*Nobody* laughs here. That is our customers' business—to laugh." And then, after giving me one more glance of stern disapproval, he turned his attention back to Fleitmann. "That little story of yours," he said, "comes out of a collection of *Eastern Jewish Tales* that my grandfather, he should rest in peace, once brought back in the fall of 1863, when he attended the great market fair at Danzig. You have any other good ones like that?"

After Fleitmann had helped himself to a second glass of tea, he told two additional stories, and when they were finished, he and Marinoff proceeded to haggle lengthily about the price for these suggested contributions. The editor felt that four dollars and a quarter was a truly generous fee for all three of these yarns, while Fleitmann stubbornly held out for six dollars flat. After three quarters of an hour they finally settled on five dollars, and the moment Fleitmann had left the office Marinoff gave off a few amused chuckles.

"Of course, those jokes of his still need quite a lot of work," he said. "But, by and large, after I get through with them, they're sure to make quite a hit with our customers. They're along a groove that everybody understands, and although I know perfectly well where he lifted them, he did save me a lot of work by going to the right sources himself. And as for you, young man," he said, turning reproachfully toward me, "I advise you not to do any laughing while jokes are being offered for sale here. Your foolish cackle cost me a whole dollar, and I certainly hope that such a thing will never happen again."

It never did. Later on I looked up Fleitmann at one of his coffeehouse hangouts, and in due time we became rather close friends. It was during one of these meetings with him at the Café Royal on Twelfth Street and Second Avenue that I voiced a long complaint about what I considered were Marinoff's shortcomings as an editor.

"For instance," I said, "every week I read all of the German, French and Hungarian humorous publications and I translate some very funny material for him and he hardly ever uses any of it."

"Well," said Fleitmann, looking at me speculatively, "you see, in this particular instance, I think you are doing him an injustice."

"What do you mean *injustice?*" I said. "I wouldn't bother with any of that stuff if it weren't really funny. After all, humor is humor, isn't it?"

"No," said Fleitmann, sticking a cigarette into his long, badly singed paper holder. "Humor is something very special, and it is particularly special among Jews. You understand that a really good Jewish joke is organized in such a fashion that its point would often be quite meaningless or, at best, would merely amount to a cheap wisecrack if it were uttered by characters who are gentiles."

"You mean that no gentile can understand a Jewish joke?" I said.

"Not at all. I'm just maintaining that the humor you read in the foreign press has to be translated into Yiddish before Marinoff can print it in *The Big Stick.*"

"And what's wrong with *that?*" I asked.

"There is nothing wrong with it, but you will just have to learn that a joke about Gaston or Alphonse, or Ching-ling-lee

284

does not automatically become a Jewish joke simply because you've decided to call the protagonists Abraham or Moishe or Irving. In fact, the chances are that in the mere transposition toward a Jewish milieu you will wind up by making a pretty strong anti-Semitic point."

"Anti-Semitic?" I said. "You think I'd translate anti-Semitic stories?"

"Of course not," said Fleitmann. "You see, the trouble with you is that because of your almost sterile upbringing you never really learned to understand the nature of Jewish humor. To encompass the whole significance of all of its facets, you must constantly keep in mind the brutal persecutions and ghettoizations which this sadly injured minority has had to undergo through the ages. Very well then, when you come to examine this matter more closely, you can plainly see that Jewish humor is basically quite different from that of all other people, since the butt of the gentile joke is generally laughed at by the *reader* or the *listener*, while the victim of the Jewish joke almost invariably laughs at *himself*. Also—and this is of the greatest importance—during the several millennia, being the helpless victim of unrelenting abuse, the Jew, by means of his peculiar sense of humor, discovered an effective prophylactic technique to achieve a state of remarkably *uncynical* disillusionment. So, in his life, which consisted of constantly unjustified major harassments, he was able to maintain a certain psychic equilibrium by his clear recognition that mankind was often motivated by purely blind and unreasonable impulses which it found subsequently convenient to rationalize into seemingly relevant social patterns. Since he was rarely placed in a position where he could *forgive* and *forget*, he just settled for a game in which logic became the pliant handmaiden of a relentlessly consistent irony. And, finally, I want you to remember that the vast majority of Jews who eked out their existences on the despairing outer fringes of almost total poverty were, nevertheless, throughout the many centuries, accused of being the secret hoarders of every sort of earthly riches. This paradox, which, I'm

285

afraid, is still unresolved, has given them a particularly unique relationship to *money*, which no other people on this earth could possibly comprehend."

"Frankly," I said, "when this conversation began I didn't realize that a simple Jewish joke could lend itself to such a completely involved and far-reaching analysis."

"Well, now you know better," said Fleitmann. "I think that every basic Jewish joke ought to contain reflections of one or even several of the elements we have been discussing. I'll try to demonstrate my meaning by telling you one story that might serve as an apt demonstration of what I have in mind. It goes like this:

"A Jewish woman asks her husband one evening to let her have some money to carry her through for the rest of the week.

"The husband gives her a puzzled look and says, 'You must think money grows like grass. I gave you five dollars just a couple of days ago; what ever happened to *that* money?'

" 'Aha!' says the wife. 'So you want to know what happened to those five dollars, eh? All right, then, take a pencil, and I'll tell you.'

"So the man takes a pencil and a piece of paper and looks expectantly at his wife.

"She first gives a little cough and says, 'A dollar *here* and a dollar *there* is *two* dollars?'

"The man bends over the paper and silently writes down two dollars.

" 'Further,' says the wife, 'before a person even turns around is *another* two dollars?'

"The husband quietly writes down two more dollars.

"Then the wife says, 'And how I spent that fifth dollar—I'm not going to tell you!'

"You see, Alex, what is particularly Jewish in this story is not the wife's seeming willfulness. Not a bit of it. What is so peculiarly Jewish about it is the husband's attitude as he silently puts those figures down on paper. And *that* is really the big point of this joke, since a Jew knows only too well that a dollar *here* and a dollar *there is, indeed, two* dollars. He knows equally well that before you turn around is *another two* dollars. This sort of arithmetic arises not only from the high cost of living in a complex social setup, it comes also from a great many centuries of bitter remembering; it comes from a time when the Jew in his ordinary daily life had to finagle and connive and bribe for almost every cup of drinking water, for the privilege of walking on certain proscribed streets, and for even the most minute violations of the curfew laws to which he and his kind were peculiarly subject. So, you see, the Jewish joke is like a psychological antiseptic that keeps the deadly bugs of fear and despair from multiplying too alarmingly in the Jew's overcrowded subconscious. And, so, when the wife tells her husband what she did with the money— tells it in a manner that would appear extraordinarily vague to any other type of husband—the Jew considers her haphazard account of the missing five dollars an almost meticulously explicit and painstaking sort of audit. In short, this joke makes its obvious point on the well-known feminine incapacity to deal with situations requiring mathematical consistency, but, besides that, it also rings the still unmuted bells of ethnic memory, which are heard *only* by the ears of Jews.

"I'll tell you another story, that also presents several of the essential ingredients for a real Jewish joke.

"One day a poor Jew called Nochem comes to his rabbi and tells him that he is in absolute despair. Nothing he undertakes seems to work out, and, as a matter of fact, he has even several times come pretty close to doubting the justice of heaven.

"The rabbi is very much upset to hear this and says to Nochem, 'Listen to me, my friend. I'm going to give you two hundred rubles, and I want you to open a store in a very busy street.'

" 'What sort of store?' says Nochem.

" 'I want you to open a store,' says the rabbi, 'where you will sell only two items: you will sell *bread* and you will sell *shrouds*. In that way it will be impossible for you to go wrong, since all living people need bread and all dead people need shrouds. Right?'

" 'You are a very wise man, Rabbi,' says Nochem.

"About a month later these two meet again, and Nochem looks even more depressed than at the time when he had come for help. The rabbi is profoundly astonished, of course, and at once asks him what has happened.

" 'Nothing happened,' says Nochem. 'I and my family are at our wits' end.'

" 'Didn't you take my advice?' says the rabbi. 'Did you open a store to sell bread and shrouds, as I told you to?'

" 'I did,' says Nochem. 'I did exactly what you advised me to do.'

" 'And then?' says the rabbi.

" 'And then—*nothing!*' says Nochem. 'You see, Rabbi, unlucky as I am, I made a terrible mistake. I opened my store in a Jewish neighborhood.'

" 'And what's wrong with that?' asks the rabbi.

" 'What's wrong with it?' says Nochem. 'In a Jewish neighborhood people don't *live* and people don't *die;* they just *suffer.*'

"You see, Alex, *that's* a joke with a really authentic Jewish flavor," said Fleitmann.

"Most of the other jokes that are told about Jews are simply socially acceptable demonstrations of open or disguised contempt for them, and the people who repeat such stories enjoy raising these verbal smoke screens merely to hide from their own selves the patently obvious fact that they are superior to nobody, not even to a cockroach."

After I'd come to know Fleitmann a good deal better, I discovered that he was a part-time music critic for one of the large New York dailies and that he also did quite a bit of translating for various book publishers around town. He brought to my attention three or four authors I had never heard of, among them Francis Jammes and Frederick Rolfe, who wrote under the name Baron Corvo. He lent me a copy of *Hadrian the Seventh* and he told me a story out of a collection called *Cruel Tales,* by Villiers de L'Isle-Adam, which he was translating from the French at that time. This man's work had only very fragmentarily been rendered into English and, as far as I could discover, his short stories were altogether unavailable in anything but French. Alfred Knopf, some years later, published a volume with the title *Sardonic Tales*, but the yarn Fleitmann told me and that I'm now going to tell you is not contained in its pages.

Villiers was a true eccentric. He came of very ancient noble lineage, and although he was almost completely penniless throughout his life, he always acted like a proud grand seigneur. A shabby top hat, a tattered cape, and frayed trousers were the total extent of his wardrobe, and it has been said by one of his contemporaries that he was the only man in Paris whose boots carried patches on their patches. At any rate, he was very touchy about his distinguished name, and woe to anyone who dared to cast the slightest aspersions on the heroic virtues of his forebears. He was a writer of great imaginative power, and as a devout Catholic and a bred-in-the-bone royalist, he had the most profound contempt for all modern innovations. He loathed democratic man, he abhorred science, and he dreaded the coming of an equalitarian society which would eradicate poetry, art and religion, in order to replace these with the poisonous vulgarities of a mechanical civilization. Curiously enough, the artist in Villiers very frequently triumphed over the prejudices and limitations of the man, and this particular tale demonstrates this quite effectively.

The story takes place in Spain, in Saragossa, at the time of the Inquisition. In the cellars of an Inquisitorial fortress the chief rabbi of the town is imprisoned on the trumped-up charge of blasphemy. The dungeon in which he languishes is three stories below the street level, and only malefactors who are definitely doomed to be burned in the public square are ever immured there. The rabbi, whose name is Jehuda Abarbanel, was arrested at four o'clock one morning during the Passover holidays, and has been kept in solitary confinement for the past three months. Only the sparsest light filters through a narrow air shaft down into this grim dungeon, and the constant dripping of water has fouled the walls and the floor of this pit with a miasmic growth partly vegetable and partly animal. The rabbi's cloak has rotted and hangs in loose strips from his gaunt frame, and his venerable beard is matted into a repulsive fungoid substance. His lips move in constant prayer, but otherwise there is no sign of life in this hunched figure, squatting on a stone bench which has been hewn out of the solid rock.

Every single afternoon throughout the passing months the Grand Inquisitor has come to call on Reb Jehuda, for all of Saragossa knows how greatly he cherishes the rabbi's immortal soul. Today he calls on him again. Accompanied by two grim friars, who carry charcoal braziers in a vain attempt to modify the icy atmosphere, the Grand Inquisitor has come to make his last visit.

"Tomorrow, my son," he says to the rabbi, who had not even raised his head when the three black-robed figures entered, "tomorrow thou wilt be burned in a grand auto-da-fé in view of thousands who are to profit by this salutary spectacle. Thou wilt go up in flames in the company of fifty-three other stubborn unbelievers, who all look to thee at this moment for a word of guidance. I pray thee, therefore, repent of thy errors—kiss this sacred cross and thou wilt die in the knowledge that eternal forgiveness and eventual salvation await not only thee but all those other misguided creatures whose spiritual misleader thou art at this moment. Repent! I beg of thee! I plead with thee on my knees to consider thy immortal soul. I weep over thee as if thou wert mine own brother—see how my tears fall upon thee, Jehuda, and know that my heart is torn in agony for thee at this moment."

The Inquisitor actually kneels down on the stony ground, and his eyes overflow with pity for the old rabbi, who sits like a graven image and never deigns to raise his eyelids. Only a sound as of the soft falling of intermittent raindrops comes from his parched and swollen lips, which have never ceased to move.

At last the Inquisitor rises to his feet and folds his hands in prayer. "May God in his wisdom and mercy grant thee a change of heart. I am bowed down with grief for thy sake, and I shall continue to beseech the favor of heaven in thy behalf." He makes the sign of the cross, turns slowly toward the huge oaken door, and, followed by the two friars, leaves the room.

For a long, long time the rabbi sits motionless, and then at last, with a most painful effort, he opens his eyes. In the dim light it seems to him that the huge bolt that secures the doorway to his dungeon has missed the iron haft for which it is intended. A shock of hope, like a bolt of inner lightning, shakes the old man's frame as he slowly lowers himself from his stone bed. If that door is really open, then his chances for escape are not altogether unlikely. He knows the internal organization of the prison like the palms of his own hands. For many years, late into the troubled nights, he has studied the plans of this dreadful structure, and since quite a few of his coreligionists have been confined in it, the additional information that a few fortunate ones have managed to bring him after their release has made him thoroughly conversant with most of its underground ramifications.

Slowly, slowly, he crawls across the moist ground like a huge insect in whose mind a great plan is beginning to ripen. At last he reaches his goal, and as he looks up his heart misses three beats: the bolt has missed its destination. The door is open!

He knows that the corridor which runs past his cell leads to a short stairway which winds toward another door, whose lock is accessible from the inside. Once beyond that last barrier, one would be standing on a wooded hill overlooking the whole town. Even a feeble and totally debilitated old man might succeed in sliding down that incline, and, favored by the dark shadows of the dense olive trees, it was, perhaps, possible for him to gain the shelter of his synagogue, where eager hearts and hands would help to spirit him toward a zone of safety. Slowly and most painfully, the rabbi continues on his hands and knees along the corridor, and he has nearly reached an empty niche along the nearest wall when he suddenly hears the sound of approaching footsteps. If only he had been able to continue for another few moments he could have crawled into that shelter and been totally invisible. However, he has no time to dwell on this misfortune, since the footsteps come closer, and at last he sees that two people are approaching from different directions—and, by still a further mischance, they stop to greet one another almost within reach of the rabbi's trembling hands.

The men are two friars connected with the servicing of the prison, and one of them, a rather stout creature who breathes with some difficulty, makes elaborate complaints about the state of his failing health. As he goes on wheezing, it seems to the terrified fugitive that this friar is looking directly into his eyes, and it suddenly comes to the mind of the poor old man that he has perhaps already died some time ago, and is, therefore, quite invisible to the mere mortal eyes of this casual blabber. But the waves of acute agony which rack his starved and tortured frame remind him, at once, that he is, indeed, only too painfully alive. And so, a moment or two after the friars have gone their different ways, he again resumes his desperate crawl toward freedom.

He is barely conscious when he finally reaches the steps he has been anticipating, and when he has at last managed to master them, he also finds the door with the readily accessible lock of his reckoning. With a strength derived from pure despair, he lifts the bolt and moves the door slowly inward. Through the ensuing opening he sees the clouded sky, and on his burning cheeks he feels the caressing night air which blows gently over Saragossa. He steps out onto a small stone terrace, and the smell of lemon blossoms comes to him from the gardens below.

The town is sleeping.

But before the rabbi is ready for his hazardous slide toward safety, he first raises his shrunken arms toward heaven to thank the omnipotent God for the grace of his benevolence.

And as he lifts up his trembling hands, a great shadow falls upon him, and while his fingers clutch at the cloth of a dark robe, he feels the sudden embrace of the Grand Inquisitor, who says to him in a voice shaken by deep sorrow: "What, my brother? On the morrow of thy deliverance, thou wouldst leave us?"

As the rabbi sinks to the ground, he realizes with his final shred of awareness that he has suffered their ultimate punitive measure—they had subjected him to The Torture of Hope.

CHAPTER TWENTY-FIVE

I KNOW QUITE a few people of considerable financial means who live in the country all the year round. Most of them aren't as young as they used to be and all of them tell me that they prefer this sort of life because it is healthier in every imaginable sort of way. No gas fumes, no parking problems, no traffic noises, no street gangs and no neighbors who throw nerve-racking parties.

Well, I discovered that nearly all of this is just so much moonshine, since a good many of these yearners for bucolic peace get drunk pretty regularly, smoke one cancer-producing cigarette after another, and never miss a chance to go to a local booze shindig even if they loathe the people who are paying for it.

The real reason for their voluntary state of retirement is the fact that they've *failed* at something. Luckily, they all have enough loot to sulk it out under the trees near their swimming pools, and if they smelled even the faintest whiff of a possible success anywhere in that ugly city of stone and asphalt, they'd break every traffic law in the books just to get down there in time.

When I say they "failed," I mean they were trying to make it not just in business; they had their sights located a little higher, in that neighborhood where commerce very frequently comes to rub shoulders with one of the arts; where the company is the best, and where the dividends are still quite likely to be substantial.

The theater works under that kind of setup, and publishing also readily qualifies under this fascinating heading. Of course, there are a goodly number of ex-orchestra leaders and ex-movie stars, too, who've decided to devote the rest of their lives to the improvement of the begonia crop. I meet them all the time. The passing parade, on its way toward more interesting (or perhaps only more sensational) manifestations has somehow managed to spit them out, and all of a sudden they're busy with Burpee's seed catalogues and they're poring over books that instruct you how to tie trout flies.

So, you'll say, "What's wrong with *that?*"

I think it's a great idea for a couple of months each year, but for people who are not professional groundkeepers or farmers it seems to me to be a pretty foolish way to waste your life.

Come on, now, let's look this thing straight in the eye: The city provides a good many nuisances—there can be no question about that—but it also supplies your soul with the nourishments of civilization, and no sane person will voluntarily throw such treasures overboard.

In the city I can go to the opera, to the concert, to the theater, to the ballet, and I can look up the name of Tiglat Pilezer's grandmother in libraries that are open till ten o'clock at night and that are the world's wonder for sheer resourcefulness and efficiency.

I will now make my final reference to those busy letter writers who so freely bombarded me with mail during the last few years. The most depressing correspondence of all came to me from small towns, in which young people felt that they were being slowly but consistently smothered. I answered most of them and told them *to acquire an education at any cost,* and then to cut out to places where the dreams in their hearts would be at least sympathetically understood, even if they were destined never to reach complete fulfillment. It goes without saying that the places I had in mind were neither Scranton nor Buffalo. I meant New York or San Francisco, where their appetites for culture would not raise the eyebrows of their gossipy, stultified neighbors completely out of normal orbit.

I've mentioned before that when my children were small we used to spend the greater part of each warm season up in the country. Sometimes we'd be there as much as three or four months at a stretch, and I must say I even used to get quite a bit of work done during those physically rather active periods.

Once I even did a bit of outdoor cooking that turned out pretty sensational in its way. It was in a place called Kent Cliffs, during the late twenties, in the fall of the year, that this event took place, and it came about chiefly because a wholesale dairy products merchant owed me a bill that he was unable to settle in cash. I had made a black-and-white poster for this character, and three days before he was pushed into bankruptcy a truck pulled up in front of our house and two extremely preoccupied and taciturn men dumped four tubs of butter, two crates of cream cheese, and twenty dozen eggs onto our croquet field.

Well, since there were only the four of us in the family and we hardly expected any more guests that late in the season, all that easily perishable stuff proved something of an embarrassment to us. Also, we had nowhere to store all that cheese and butter so that it could be kept from turning rancid.

At this critical juncture in our lives a great thought came to me. You see, some weeks before, while rummaging around in an abandoned shack along our road, my children had discovered an enormous metal pan nearly six feet across and about ten inches high. I imagine the original owner had required a vessel of such unusual proportions as a fermenting vat for his outsize bootlegging operations. That was the way I explained it to myself, although a visiting friend of ours expressed the opinion that it was far more likely that my kids had stumbled onto a defunct counterfeiting plant. Well, for quite a while I couldn't imagine what possible use we might ever come to make of this enormous hunk of kitchenware, but in the meanwhile, with the help of a neighbor's tow truck, we had moved that pan provisionally over behind our kitchen garden.

And then, after all that unexpected cow-and-chicken-produce had landed right on top of us, I suffered a sudden inspiration:

I would bake a pie—*in that dish!*

Nobody was terribly enthusiastic about the idea when I first announced it. Of course it is perfectly understandable, too, since the whole concept was on a scale for which most ordinary imaginations are completely out of training. If you had seen that pot with your own eyes, chances are you also might have boggled at my casually announced suggestion. Fortunately for me, I was never yet stopped from doing anything merely because there happened to be a unanimous feeling around the place that it had better not be done.

However, I'll tell you what really turned the tide in my favor, and that was the fact that we were at the height of the apple harvest and there was nobody anywhere near us who bothered to do any harvesting. We were all slithering around on the half-rotten fruit, and my stupendous plan at once gave real meaning and purpose to all of nature's rich bounty.

And you know how it is with a truly hot idea: no sooner had the brilliance of it come clearly through to everyone's mind than a dozen pairs of willing hands were instantly mine to command. Of course, these hands belonged mostly to children who were in the ideal position of being under school age at that time.

The rest is culinary history.

I baked the largest apple pie extant in America in the year 1927. It wasn't easy. But I can tell you right now that we were completely successful.

That pie was six feet in diameter and ten inches deep, and its construction consumed sixteen bags of flour, ten pounds of sugar, twelve pounds of butter, ten pounds of cream cheese and ten dozen eggs. Don't bother telling me that those eggs were super-fluous, since I'm sure your experience with pastry of such size is probably pretty limited. All I know is that it was a truly unique recipe, of which no one has bothered to avail himself since. I can't remember at the moment how many bushels of apples we peeled for this occasion, but I can tell you that I used up ten large boxes of raisins and ten ounces of powdered cinnamon, and I even grated into this mixture the skins of twenty-four good-sized lemons.

Since I couldn't imagine myself making a top crust for this monster, I just rolled out some long bands of that flaky dough and laid them crisscross from rim to rim. Each length of that fancy latticework was as thick as a hawser rope and, after it was all done, even just a couple of bites of it were enough to ruin your appetite for supper.

Now then, I forgot to tell you that, with the help of a couple of hired men, we placed this dish very cunningly on top of some good-sized stones and, afterward, we proceeded to light a very moderate fire under it. We used wood, pinecones and a few bags of coal, and at the suggestion of one of the children we had armed ourselves with half a dozen pairs of bellows, just to keep things going properly and in style.

It was a big job.

The youngsters and I had to take turns during the night to see that everything was progressing in an orderly fashion, and when the sun came up the next morning the pie was done.

I don't think that, offhand, anybody could imagine what sort of things started to happen to us as the result of that dizzy piece of cookery.

First of all, people driving along the roads, even six or seven miles away, would raise their heads in a confused surmise and start sniffing the air like a bunch of suddenly alerted bird dogs. Don't you see, in the country the average driver is used to smell-ing gasoline fumes or skunks or maybe some overripe cow barns —but apple pie is really a little out of the ordinary. If the wind was in the right direction, this odor would carry all the way over to the main highway that led on to New York, and a whole world of famished uncles and their giggling nieces would set about to pursue this tantalizing smell to its original source.

Although we were located way off on a steep little dirt road, by the late afternoon of that first day a whole slew of cars had started to pile up on us, and long before that steaming vat of pastry had had a chance to cool down, people from five states, two of them west of the Mississippi, were smacking their lips in eager anticipation of the joys to come.

The funny thing was that although we handed out good-sized samplings of our specialty to everyone who was willing to eat, by nightfall only about a quarter of it had been consumed. Luckily, we had a lot of white gauze stored away in our attic, so we stretched some layers of this stuff across the top and sides of our pie dish, and, believe me, it was high time that we took this measure, because flies, beetles and bees were beginning to congregate by the thousands, trying to stake out claims for themselves and their families, from county seats as far away as Albany.

The weather continued fair for the next thirty-six hours, and so nothing particularly untoward took place until the night of the second day. We used to build a small fire every afternoon—only enough, really, to heat up the pan and give the stuff some of its original aroma—and then, during one night, a truly unexpected thing happened.

You see, during those peculiar years a lot of people had abandoned their farms and gone off to the city to work in various factories, and so it came about that quite a number of formerly domestic animals had learned to fend for themselves in those neglected fields and meadows that were reverting back to nature all about us. Well, during the third night of the apple-pie equinox, a couple of spavined horses and a superannuated cow, whose udder looked like an empty reticule, decided to remove the protective covering from our oversized chafing dish and to help themselves to a load of unexpected goodies.

Of course, by that time everybody in that neighborhood had

had his sufficient fill of that special form of dessert, and so none of us begrudged those homeless disasters their stolen treats.

The trouble came when we discovered that unusual grub of that sort doesn't sit too well with most herbivorous critters. It seems to give them absolutely disastrous charges of internal gas, and so, for the next few nights none of us was able to catch a wink of sleep. The alarming rumblings and occasional booming diapasons that emanated from those gluttonous derelicts, all suffering from agonies of colic, of course, were simply not to be ignored. The animals refused to move away from the scene of their crime and just leaned up against our front porch like prodigal gasbags that had come home to die.

I finally had to pay a nearby farmer to lead those convulsed tympanies away from our property, and when, a couple of days later, a swarm of wasps started to build a nest over the remains of that pastry, we decided to pack up our belongings and move back to town.

Still, sometimes, when my children and I get together, I'm pleased that they well remember our experiment in large-scale outdoor baking, and when my grandchildren look up at us in palpably bug-eyed envy as we describe our first cut into that six-foot apple pie I have the feeling that it was all well worth the little trouble it had cost us.

At any rate, you can clearly see that our lives were not exactly humdrum.

CHAPTER TWENTY-SIX

AND NOW THAT this book of mine is heading down the homestretch, I want to tell you a few of my ideas on the subject of The Company Man.

Well over twenty years ago I used to work in the *idea* department of *Life* magazine. I came to know most of the people who sat in the diminutive cubicles along editorial row, and I was on very good terms with the office boys, and even the poor bedeviled girls who worked in the unbelievably harassed picture department became quite friendly with me.

After a while, I noticed that, no matter how badly misunderstood and abused any of these laborers in the Luce vineyards felt themselves to be, they all had, nevertheless, a certain *esprit de corps*, a demonstrably ever-present feeling that they belonged to a chosen elite, and they unquestionably believed that they were somehow *in* on things to which the common herd of non-Luce employees were forever doomed to aspire in vain.

I spent quite a bit of time trying to figure out how and why this grotesque notion had first originated, and by what mysterious propulsion of elaborate self-deception it had managed to keep up its unabated momentum. In the end I came to the conviction that most of my colleagues actually not only had a profound disesteem for the executive masterminds who steered and manipulated the organization which employed them but also suspected and loathed most of the people who worked alongside them, and finally I even became thoroughly convinced that they all really had a pretty poor opinion of themselves, too.

Hence, their elaborately reared structure of arrogance was something in the nature of a protective wall which successfully isolated them from a world in which everyone was responsible for his opinions and attitudes and in which the foolish practitioners took daily chances on their own accounts, without the benefit of a powerful corporate image to shield them.

If anybody ever said, "I work on *Life*," and even uttered this statement with a *moue* of almost obligatory embarrassment, it nevertheless carried the unspoken implications that the speaker was steadily employed, that his severance pay was guaranteed by contract, that he was the beneficiary of chronologically established salary increases, and, above all else, that he was a minor satellite in a major galaxy whose light illuminated (and sometimes very deliberately distorted) all of visible creation.

In short, by merely mentioning the bare fact of one's employment, one automatically achieved a status identification with an enormously puissant communications apparatus whose far-reaching tentacles were likely to probe, almost unchecked, into every photographable corner of the universe.

You've got to admit that this must be pretty heady wine for people who are destined to achieve no particular standing in our society by their own competitively identifiable efforts.

Of course, the photographers who work for such an outfit can, to a certain degree, be called exempt from the more miasmic implications contained in this exordium. Their work guarantees them a measure of identity, and although they have no say at all over the ultimate use of their pictures, they are inordinately well paid and, at least, their demonstrably personal efforts manage to achieve occasional recognition in the body of the magazine.

A little while ago, when I had good reason to pass through the Time and Life Building, one of their researchers, who has known me for quite a number of years, stopped to give me greetings.

I talked to her for a few minutes, and during our brief confab a few of her fellow employees passed by us in the lobby and gave me, personally, the sort of smiles which used to make me good and sick in the days when I still worked there.

Such a smile is full of the *insider's* supercilious smugness toward anyone who doesn't belong to the fashionable frat; or for anybody who is just stumbling along blindly, in a catch-as-catch-can world, as a disaffiliated schmoe; who has no officially assigned niche in which a good paycheck is delivered at definitely regulated periods; whose existence is just a daily series of blind risks without any of the obvious security and prestige concomitants which are derived from association with an internationally recognized publicity apparatus.

As I've already told you, I used to wonder about those smiles in 1937 and 1940 (inclusively), and I couldn't help feeling a little sad over the thought that this whole insecure mob of nonentities —these people who were never allowed to sign their names to anything they had perpetrated—should be compelled, by their own personal disasters, to place little, if any, value on anyone else's recognizable meritorious endeavors.

I realize, of course, that such a state of intracorporate exclusiveness is indigenous to all large and well-organized human enterprises, but let us admit that only in a very few of them is there so vast a pretense that the activities of its members are laden with momentous, sociointellectual significance.

I know perfectly well that the guy who works for General Motors isn't one damned bit more enlightened or better off, but at least he doesn't presume to speak denigratingly in the public prints about great artists or playwrights, and he certainly doesn't have a chance to spill his venom over renowned scholars and distinguished national leaders. On *Time* and *Life* he can do this with absolute impunity, since he operates from behind the safe ambush of his journalese anonymity.

That there shall always be Company Men with poison-pen privileges is an evil that we may have to go on suffering in our society, but, please, let us at least remember to look askance upon these special creatures who seem to flourish so exuberantly in this mephitic moral morass.

And, finally, when such individuals go abroad in the land and some innocent wayfarer happens to come too close to their persons, then let them sound off their rattles of alarm, and let them be compelled to cry out: "Unclean! Unclean! Unclean!"

In the last few years I have read about a dozen books on the deplorable effects of insidiously omnipresent Company mores on the psychic equilibrium of the overintegrated individual.

In plainer terms, the well-intentioned authors of these volumes deplore the stultifying results of what I have generally come to call *Total Employment.*

Well, I can only tell you that it is my considered opinion that the majority of people have always yearned for exactly this sort of cotton-wool padding to protect their earthly meanderings, and that most of the worthy men who analyze these conditions tend to make a generic dilemma out of their highly individualistic findings, and occasionally they even manage to justify, quite logically, some of their own purely personal frustrations.

Actually, there is no historic basis to sustain the highly romantic thesis that man is simply busting apart with longings to realize his precious and unique individuality. I think such an assumption rests on a complete falsehood. What most men want is to be free from financial worries, and if, in addition to this boon, any prospective employers are also inclined to offer them gratuitous medical care and more than adequate retirement funds, they will not only be content but hysterically eager to sign up for the duration of whatever the hell happens to be going on.

And, what's more, you can't really blame them for that either. The tragedy is that very few people ever really become aware of their precious individuality and, with the passing of skilled handicrafts, even the last remnants of individual assertiveness seem to have fallen by the way. Of course, each man believes that he is as good as anybody else—and maybe even a lot better—but he is certainly not prepared to put this easily verifiable concept to any sort of crucial test. He wouldn't risk the safety of his family to prove this superiority of his, and if he has to suppress his extraordinary uniqueness for the sake of a good, steady job, he is certainly going to.

Naturally in the premachine age it was easier to give play to personal quirks and eccentricities of all sorts, but once mechanization had become the most powerfully commanding factor of our daily lives, the odd and the peculiar were simply doomed to extinction. You can afford to be indulgent toward whimsy in an old-fashioned buggy-whip factory maybe, but certainly a modern corporation which hopes to maintain itself successfully will not be in the mood to jeopardize its enormous investments merely to give free play to the time-consuming idiosyncrasies of its individualistically inclined employees.

That's just common sense.

So what's to be done?

Let's think about it for a minute.

We know that the millions of undernourished people all over the world would like nothing better than to have themselves confronted by a problem like ours. In fact, I'm sure that they dream about nothing else. On the other hand, it is certainly undeniable that despite the cozy comforts that envelop our lives, there is a good deal of frustration rampant in our midst. I indicated the reasons for this a good while back, in the very earliest chapters of this book. It seems to me also that, despite all hopeful statistics to the contrary, organized religion is becoming a less and less significant factor in the lives of ordinary people. In certain respects, I have to confess, this represents a real loss for those among us who have nothing else to put in its place. This means that we now have a spiritual vacuum where once there had been meaningful order, and in addition to this, we have not been able to find any satisfactory substitutes for ceremonies and rituals which, besides all else, carried for a good many people the reassuring promises of personally attainable salvation.

The psychiatrist's couch, no matter how possibly useful it may prove to be, is, at best, just a leather-covered altar on which the human ego is sacrificed in the clinical fumes of Pressing Social Necessity. As a matter of fact, most psychiatric endeavors nowadays are bent toward integrating the willfully errant psyche into a world which can no longer afford to tolerate even comparatively harmless deviations.

Again—what can we do?

We can think about all this clearly, and without resorting to a lot of hypocritical asides, and without maintaining a ballast of contradictory afterthoughts, we must speak to our children truthfully about the values that have outlived Babylon and Greece and Rome, and that will certainly outlast this civilization, too, if there will be anyone left on this earth to know anything about it.

And what *are* these values?

They are the great truths which no scientific breakthrough can either modify or extinguish.

They are the truths which tell us that the most useful lives ever lived were devoted to the betterment of man's life on this earth.

They are the truths that spread knowledge and teach respect for the awful mystery residing not only in each human being but also in every animal, insect, flower, rock, cloud and sky that our senses are privileged to perceive during our brief sojourn on this perishable globe.

Above all else, we must stop pretending that a cute drum majorette is the equal or even the superior of an honor graduate who accepts, with blushing modesty, the scholarship she has attained through her zeal for learning.

We must stop believing that a high-scoring, beer-guzzling, bowling-alley bigmouth is preferable to a man who takes a group of children to the park, where he patiently and lovingly alerts their young faculties to the ceaseless wonders perceptible in nature.

We must stop lying to ourselves about our many failings and we must learn to give up our false concepts and consolations, which, in the end, will only leave us empty-handed and bitterly defrauded.

We must proceed to purge ourselves of all false ambitions and start a great housecleaning inside our cluttered identities, so that the pollinating thoughts of the noblest of mankind will have room to fructify in our foolishly bewildered hearts.

We have no other hope.

We will either come to accept the clarities and charities which spring from real wisdom, or we will perish like gluttonous dung beetles permanently sealed up in a casket full of overripe horse apples.

CHAPTER TWENTY-SEVEN

I HAVE ONLY a little space left to say my thanks to the great numbers of people who have been kind to me and to those many others who have sent me their hopeful thoughts and good wishes. I am very grateful to all of them.

During the past five years I have told you quite a bit about my life, and I am eager to believe that you have learned a few useful things from my recital. If you have not, it is more than likely to be your own fault. Try not to be too kind to yourself, since it is always possible that the people around you care either too much or too little to tell you the absolute truth.

And, as for my plans for the future—I am only anxious to go on working as long as my life lasts.

You see, I'm not a *senior citizen*. I stoutly maintain my right to be a very sick but desperately energetic *old man*, and because I feel that I'm about as totally realistic as I can afford to be, I naturally haven't any long-term projects in view at all.

But in ending this last installment of my autobiography, I should like to tell you about a time, almost thirty years ago, when, quite by accident, I happened to make one of the most important discoveries of my whole life.

It was, in fact, during the mid-thirties, and I was living on the island of Haiti in a little mountain village situated a short distance from the city of Port au Prince. My house had a most unusually picturesque location, and out of my sixteen windows I commanded a view the memory of which sends me into raptures to this very day.

My visit to the island had originally been planned to be of only very short duration, but, like a man trapped in a maze of sheer lyrical enchantment, I finally remained in my mountainside eyrie, adrift in the waving crowns of the giant palms, for the entire summer.

At any rate, early one morning, the morning of the Fourth of July, as I stepped out to have breakfast on my sun-speckled veranda, a truly astonishing sight offered itself to my vision. You see, about a thousand feet from where I stood, an enormous monolith, like a weather-smoothed prehistoric pillar, rose straight out of the valley below, right up to my very eye level. And now, as I gazed at it, I realized with a shock that someone, at some time during the past twenty-four hours, had painted in large red letters a rather cryptic message on the highest part of this geological veteran.

This is what confronted me:

URSUIT OF HAPPINESS!

Although, by this time, I had become rather inured to certain peculiarly Haitian eccentricities, I found myself completely bewildered by this newest manifestation, and it was only later in the day, when I attended a Fourth of July party on the estate of a resident American, that the matter was finally cleared up for me.

This man, whose name was Tom Feldecker, had originally come to the island because it happened to be a stipulated stopover in his Caribbean cruise, but he had at that time found the place so altogether to his liking that he had decided to settle down here permanently. He eventually came to own quite a bit of land, and he and his very attractive and sprightly wife, Melanie, were well known for their generous hospitality. Tom had made his pile in the furniture business back in the States, and his still exuberant vitality was clearly manifest in the relentless improvements he was constantly organizing on his various properties. He was a short, somewhat high-blooded character whose energies seemed completely undiminished by the tropical climate, and his dark myopic eyes always bounced around rather restlessly behind his thickly framed goggles.

As I stepped out of his living room and stood on the terrace, which faced toward my own side of the valley, the conundrum of the fractured message on the monolith became instantly comprehensible. What I now saw written, in late-afternoon sunlight, was the following:

LIFE LIBERTY AND THE P

"He's a well-meaning fool, that Jean François, isn't he?" said Tom as he came up beside me. "He did an excellent job under very difficult conditions, but he just hasn't very much judgment unless things are very carefully explained to him. If you look closely, you can even see some blue and white stars he put all around that lettering, and I must say he certainly worked like a beaver to get it done on time."

"It looks great," I said. "When I first saw it this morning I nearly fell into my cereal."

"Ah, well, that's just some of his darn-fool silliness," said Tom. "You weren't supposed to see any of it at all. All that printing was meant to be visible just from this side of the valley, and it never even occurred to me that he would be foolish enough to go on painting right onto the other side."

"It doesn't matter in the least," I said. "We're all getting a big bang out of it; don't doubt that for a moment."

"Well, it has to be erased tomorrow anyway," said Tom. "I had permission to put it up for the day, but I promised to remove it right after the Fourth. Maybe, if I'm still around, we'll do a better job next year."

"Don't worry," I said. "You'll be around for a long time. Your sort always has a lot of ginger left, and you'll live to put red paint on a lot more things than just an isolated cliff out in the valley."

"Well, I hope so," said Tom. "Come on; let's go down to my west field. I want to show you the water tank we're planning to raise next week."

Incidentally, this Jean François, the cliff painter, who was an all-around factotum on the Feldecker place, had once been immured as an incurable psychopath at the local asylum. In fact, after he had attacked and nearly killed one of the caretakers at that establishment, he had been permanently confined in a solitary cell for nearly three years. And then one day a well-heeled uncle of Jean's had turned up from a distant part of the island, and to everyone's intense surprise, had offered to send his nephew to Florida for some possibly curative treatments. The doctors on the mainland had notified Jean's benefactor that the only hope for the boy lay in rather drastic surgery. In short, they suggested a prefrontal lobotomy. After considerable voting among the various members of the family, it was finally decided that this extreme step should be taken. Three months later Jean François returned home, and although he seemed strangely muted and in certain special ways somewhat unpredictable, he had in due time become a useful member of Haitian society and was, indeed, as everyone perfectly well knew, very highly regarded by both the Feldeckers.

After the party that night, I went home and silently, and quite alone, sat out under the full moon for a very long while. I could still see that lettering quite clearly, and as I kept staring across the valley I found myself somehow rather deeply disturbed by my thoughts of

URSUIT OF HAPPINESS!

What about it? Were the Founding Fathers right? Could it really be pursued?

310

No, I finally decided. They had, all of them, been gifted and well-intentioned men, but on this particular point they had most certainly been—absolutely dead wrong.

Happiness is completely above guarantees.

It is not a right.

It is not a privilege.

It is, in most cases, just the glorious *by-product* of a benignly purposeful human life.

The man who sets his mind on achieving it is already lost, for it will not stand still, to be either captured or cajoled, and it will shed its unexpected beneficence only on the totally unself-conscious. That is why it is so difficult to encompass happiness at the moment when it occurs.

It happens as the result of———?

And then, later on, perhaps a long time afterward, it may suddenly rush to your mind that you had inadvertently entertained one of the blessed angels of the Lord.

I spent many hours thinking about all this, and I couldn't help wondering who among my large acquaintanceship might be fairly accounted as leading a truly happy life.

It wasn't an easy matter to decide offhand, and I settled, at last, to pondering just on the various existences with which I had become familiar during my long stay on the island. There was Tom Feldecker, for instance. He was rich, he had a fine wife, he was constantly occupied, and, what is more, he was greatly respected by all members of the community. His health was sound, and his children, back in the United States, seemed, certainly, to be doing well.

But *there* was the fatal chink in his armor: the children. They were, as far as I could determine, normally intelligent, reasonably ambitious, and utterly devoted to each other and to their loving and profoundly concerned parents. But Feldecker, a self-made man of the old school, a man who had wrested a fortune from a business where others had been glad to settle for a mere livelihood, continued to hover in spirit over his absent brood and found that there was a sad lack in each of his offspring which sometimes nearly drove him to the edge of despair. His sons seemed to him to be deficient in vitality and in proper manly resolve; his daughters agitated his life with innocent reports of trifling social difficulties, and their minor scholastic hurdles filled him with rages of blind frustration. The very virtues which had sustained Tom and had finally brought him to the heights of success were now becoming vices with which he tormented both himself and his bewildered family.

His fantastic nervous endurance, his capacity for sustained labor under profoundly discouraging circumstances, and, above all, his gift of imaginative anticipation of circumstances which were beyond his immediate control—all these endowments coupled to his energetic fervor were now used for the harassment of his unfortunate dependents. Since his restlessness was largely uncontrollable, he could not stand idly by while they attempted to plow some faltering furrows in their own chosen fields of endeavor. His erstwhile gifts eventually became the bane of their lives. Agitated by heaven only knows what impulses sprung from the sudden promptings of his chronic unease, he would fly back to the States every few weeks and proceed to create sheer havoc among his demoralized and frightened children.

No. There really wasn't any question about it: Tom Feldecker was far from being a happy man.

Who else?

Well, I knew a couple of honeymooners who were staying at the Souffle de Zephyr, and I even had a luncheon appointment with them for the following day. His name was Felix Herter and he was working in the advertising business back in New York City. Her name was Elsa, and the two of them made quite a handsome ensemble as they gravitated seductively around the hotel swimming pool. They had known each other for quite a few years before they were married, and I had to confess to myself that I had already discovered a certain *langueur* if not a state of actual weariness in their brand-new relationship. I could very easily guess the cause for this strange state of affairs. You see, they had already been living together for more than three years before they decided to make their condition legal, and during that comparatively hectic period they had been compelled to use a great variety of elaborate subterfuges to make the consummation of their desires possible. Now then, it stands to reason that during that time a certain breathlessly sustained atmosphere of erotic tension had enveloped most of their activities and had given their illicit relationship a poignantly romantic character. Well, that was all over now. They were free to do any damned thing they pleased, and they could go when—and wherever—they chose, and, as I could very plainly recognize, they found the whole situation something of a letdown.

They were honeymooners, all right, but, unfortunately, their first tremulous *rapprochements* had happened too long ago to endow them with anything but an aura of nostalgic regrets. Also, since both of them were extremely good-looking, they constantly required an audience and, I think, they really felt much happier when they were able to have some additional people around.

So, the honeymooners didn't qualify either.

I went through half a dozen more names that came to my mind during that ruminative session out under the bright stars, and I couldn't find a single person whom I would have pronounced truly happy. It had turned quite late and the moon had already disappeared behind the mountains when I finally thought of Dr. Price Mars, the internationally known Negro anthropologist.

I had read some of his books long before I had come to visit the islands even for the first time, and in due course I'd had the good fortune to make his acquaintance. Only a week before, I had called on him at his home in the hills above Port au Prince, and it was on this occasion that I happened, quite by accident, to overhear a certain unscheduled talk relating to his proposed candidacy for the Haitian parliament.

Dr. Price Mars had written extensively on the Carib cultures, and he was one of the outstanding authorities on the pre-Columbian Indian arts. When I dropped in on him I had found him standing on a grass plot behind his house, quietly feeding some parched corn to his small flock of guinea hens. He was a very distinguished-looking man whose close-cropped white hair accentuated the beautifully even tone of his dark face, and when we shook hands he smiled into my eyes with the wonderfully trusting candor one often sees in the faces of great *savants*.

"There is a small committee coming to see me in a little while," he said, "and although I have set this afternoon aside for you, I'm sure you wouldn't be too disturbed by a short interruption."

"I'll be glad to come some other time," I said. "I really see no reason why we can't meet a little later in the week, if that is more convenient for you."

"Not at all," he said. "They won't be here very long, and meanwhile, my wife will serve you a little refreshment while I talk briefly to these people."

Sure enough, in about half an hour three men came out into the yard and Dr. Price Mars withdrew with them to a nearby covered patio. Mrs. Price Mars, a handsome, middle-aged woman, did her best to entertain me with fruits and some homemade cakes, but, after a few minutes, our strained conversation came completely to a halt, for we couldn't help overhearing every word that was being uttered on the other side of the flimsy partition which separated us from her husband and his visitors.

Dr. Price Mars had spoken to me in beautifully articulated English, and now I heard him using the most mellifluously enunciated French for his three callers.

"I must beg you to consider my position, gentlemen," he said. "I am an oldish sort of man and I am in the midst of a work which has absorbed me for many years. My notes are almost illegible and no one could possibly decipher them if I were gone. This is my constant worry. The honor you do me moves me deeply, and, as you know, I have on several previous occasions tried to put my humble faculties at the service of our country. On these occasions I have always had to neglect my own deepest concerns for the sake of what I considered to be my public duty. But now I feel I have only enough energy left to complete a task which is very close to my heart. As you know, I live here in almost total seclusion, and I have neither the strength nor the desire to participate in any activities which threaten to take me away from my work.

My needs are very small and, happily, we have managed so well that I can at last see myself at liberty to pursue my tasks free from any worldly interruptions. So, again, I am profoundly honored by your call, and I send my best wishes and greetings to all of your respected colleagues."

Before Dr. Price Mars rejoined us, his wife said, "Thank God it is over. He loves, best of all, to sort and classify his pre-Columbian collection, and when the weather is good he sits out here and does his work. We see a few very old friends, and once in a while some teachers drop in on us, and occasionally some of their brightest pupils are allowed to come, too, because my husband believes that the future of Haiti lies in their hands."

"I believe the future of the whole world lies in their hands," said Dr. Price Mars as he returned to us. "I have divided my days into such pleasantly productive patterns that I can't bear to think that they might be upset by anything. Of course, I was never what is called ambitious, but one of the great privileges of my life nowadays is that no one has the right to expect that I should do anything but what pleases the both of us best. You see, Mr. King, I was once connected with the Haitian Embassy to the United States, and on the train trip to Washington, D.C., most of the passengers in my Pullman sleeper left their shoes to be cleaned in front of my door. It is understandable, too, since the majority of them had probably never seen a Negro on such a deluxe train who was not also a porter. So, I think I have done my share for the public service, and I certainly feel entitled to humor my own wishes at last."

After I had left the house and stood on a hill overlooking their tidy property, I could see that the great anthropologist had once more returned to feeding some kernels of parched corn to his beautifully marked guinea hens.

Price Mars is a happy man, I decided, and his wife is certainly a happy woman.

And then, as if this affirmative conclusion had tempted my mind into more fortuitous channels of reconnaissance, the name of Doc Reser suddenly popped into my head.

He was known locally as a queer case.

You must understand that the majority of the so-called native upper-class people in Haiti were hopeless snobs. Most of them were mulattoes, and even the ones who were rather dark skinned had wives who were almost white. It was an instantly discernible status symbol with them. When, many years before, I had come to the island for the first time, I discovered that although I would certainly have married any native girl that I might have fallen in love with, a goodly number among the indigenous population would definitely have drawn the color line against any women who were not as fair as their biased fancies anticipated. An attitude of this sort quite naturally entailed some absolutely hideous results. I have known some upper-class Haitian parents who hid some of their darker children in the attic when company came, and, as a direct consequence of this sick state of mind, anyone who became unduly friendly with the black peasantry or the town proletariat was sure to earn the opprobrium of the local elite.

And this was exactly what had happened to Doc Reser.

He had originally arrived in Haiti as a member of the United States occupation forces which finally came to stay in the island for nearly nineteen years. When, after this period of time, the men had been withdrawn, Doc Reser stayed on to become chief supervisor of the native insane asylum.

He had been a pharmacist's mate in our armed forces and had, over the years, developed such deep sympathy and affection for the brutally neglected Haitian masses that in the end he had decided to remain with them in any capacity of possible helpfulness.

I am not telling you any of this from hearsay.

I knew him well. I lived in his house and I spent many hours talking to him out at the asylum, which, during those days, was located in the slum and jungle periphery which was typical of some of the outer sections around Port au Prince. When I met him he was no longer in the army; he was a paid employee of the Haitian republic.

I am sixty-three years old now, and I can tell you in all fairness that in the long time that I've known and studied Haitian affairs, that unfortunate country has never enjoyed even a fractionally decent national government.

Even so, those totally corrupt political machinators were glad to pay Doc Reser his scant measure of allotted wages, because he did the work of at least a dozen men and, what is more, he kept the patients under his care in a state of self-imposed restraint which was the marvel of the whole medical faculty.

When I first caught sight of him he had just discovered the pleasures of painting. Since he had no art materials of any kind, he used to distill his colors out of flowers and roots, and his first brush had been contrived out of a swatch of his own hair, which he had fastened onto a kitchen match.

His pictures had a true primitive quality, and you may believe me that the Haitian artists who have, in the meantime, become widely touted neoprimitives have only with very rare exceptions turned out anything better than he did. You see, since those benighted years that I am speaking about, the island has flourished into a sort of cultural renaissance. Not a political or financial one, just an artistic one—and you're liable to read about that pictorial florescence at any moment in the magazine sections of some of the American Sunday newspapers.

At any rate, I had ample opportunities to see how Doc Reser spent most of the pay that the constantly shaky Haitian governments used to dole out to him. He gave a large part of it to the people who worked around the asylum, and another good share of it went to buy cigarettes for his totally impoverished patients. At least once a week he also had some of the best drummers in the land come out to his compound, and the dancing and the singing that took place on these occasions was really something to behold.

"Drumming and dancing is their life," he said to me. "Years ago, when the people whose slaves they were prevented them from carving gods for themselves, the natives just settled for making drums, and I can tell you they put all of their thwarted aspirations into this single remaining channel for racial self-expression. I think they are absolute masters at it."

They were, indeed.

Later on I discovered that Doc Reser sometimes drummed and danced along with the best of them, and of course the natives adored him. I don't mean the color-conscious ones, who gambled nightly for high stakes in the Port au Prince country club; I mean the common working stiffs who talked only Creole and who labored for about twenty cents a day at jobs that would have killed many an animal raised for that purpose. In some of their semi-outdoor furniture shops I saw *hand*-operated lathes being propelled for ten and twelve hours at a stretch, and only Doc Reser ever seemed to ask himself whether the men who performed this sort of work were not also, perhaps, entitled to be included among those for whom Christ had made his stupendous symbolic sacrifice.

"I tell you, I would never have allowed them to have that lobotomy performed on Jean François," he once said to me.

"He nearly killed a man," I said.

"Well," he said, "some of the things that used to go on here would have provoked a saint. You see, Jean François was the feeblest of twelve children, and I know that he had never received any sort of kindness from anybody. I suppose he's all right now, and the Feldeckers are certainly very nice to him. Just the same, to take the prefrontal lobes out of a man's head—something that may have taken twenty million years to develop—seems like a pretty desperate sort of thing to do. Doesn't it?"

Well, as I sat there in that mild tropical night, thinking about all these matters, I realized that I had found another absolutely happy man. Doc was fulfilling himself, completely, in his affectionate concern for people who would have been utterly friendless without him, and, as far as I could see, he was their only effective bulwark against an otherwise indifferent and even hostile world.

I recalled the last time I had seen him. There was a totally leafless tree out in the back yard of the asylum, and, as if by common agreement, the skinny, permanently molting chickens in the whole dreary neighborhood used to come to roost in it. It was a truly weird sight to see all that bankrupt poultry covering every branch and twig of that dead cottonwood tree, and the day I happened to drop by, Doc was sitting just a little distance away, doing a painting of this apocalyptic manifestation.

He was a chunky type of man, very blue-eyed and extremely fair skinned, and his close-cropped hair was so white that one sometimes discovered with surprise that a few blond stubbles were still left in it.

As I watched him I could see almost tangible emanations of pure joy radiating from his pink countenance, which was puckered into folds of amiable concentration. His huge, freckled hand held his tiny brush in creative hesitancy above the piece of cardboard he had propped up against a convenient stone, and as I looked at him I was convinced that Adam, on that first day, in that first garden, could have known no greater happiness than this.

I might as well confess that somewhere in the recesses of my heart I have for a long time nursed the suspicion that *real happiness* can only be known by the compassionate and the brave, and that all the rest is merely idle chatter.

Of course, I am fully aware that it can come to children at any time—on a sandpile, at a picnic, or even while sitting absolutely still in the crown of a flowering cherry tree.

And, just because children sometimes seem like wistful refugees from a more amiable planet, I do most earnestly beseech you to treat them with judicious care.

Consider that *the happiness of all mankind* may, even now, be trembling in the scales of some possible tomorrows.

I was writing these last few pages outdoors, in the rear of our house, when a besotted firefly seemed suddenly to have fallen in love with the burning end of my cigarette. I regret that as the result of this disastrous infatuation, he perished, almost instantly.

I must say that I find this trivially symbolic event an altogether appropriate epilogue to a good many of my painstaking admonishments and conjectures.

So, until further notice: "Hail, and Farewell!"